RAILWAY SAFETY

HM Railway Inspectorate's
Annual Report on the safety record
of the railways in Great Britain
during 1992/93

HSE
BOOKS

© Crown copyright 1993
Applications for reproduction should be made to HMSO
First published 1993

ISBN 0 7176 0651 1

The cover of this report is a reproduction of a visual
display unit signal diagram of Paddington Station, as
seen in the controlling signal box at Swindon.
Superimposed on this is a photograph of the modified
track and signal layout, showing a high speed train
approaching the refurbished Paddington Station.

(Courtesy of British Railways Board)

CONTENTS

Continued overleaf

FOREWORD

This report, while not all good news, does convey a substantially improving overall picture of safety on the railways.

Readers of the last annual report will be aware that the statistics are now collated on the basis of the financial year. Therefore this report covers the period from 1 April 1992 to 31 March 1993. My predecessor, Mr R J Seymour, was HM Chief Inspecting Officer of Railways until his retirement in early February 1993, thus to him must go the credit for conducting the affairs of the Inspectorate for virtually all of that time. He is to be thanked for the significant influence he brought to bear on British Railways (BR) and the Railway Industry Advisory Committee (RIAC) over several years, to improve, for example, the safety of trackside workers. He would be the first to say that many others had a hand in this and that there is still room for improvement, but the fact is that it was largely his initiative that has reversed the unacceptable upward trend in accidents and encouraged a new awareness of safety amongst the staff on the line.

I am pleased to report that no passenger was killed in a train accident (such as a collision or derailment) on any railway in England, Scotland or Wales during the period under review. However, 26 passengers were killed by moving trains which is half the number of the previous year. A total of 50 people, including 11 railway staff, were killed in the working of the railways. Both these figures are the lowest on record. In general, however, the circumstances leading to the accidents in which they died leave much to be desired. The details are discussed in Chapter 10. Following HSE's detailed study of slam-door rolling stock, and adoption by BR of HSE's recommendations, the number of people killed falling from such coaches when running, reduced to nine last year from 19 in each of the previous four years.

However, not all the trends are good; some of the statistics relating to permanent way defects and fires, both trackside and on trains, are of concern. There has been a 30% increase in station and lineside fires and a 50% increase in incidents resulting from vandalism. The total of failures of the infrastructure etc has increased by 16%.

These matters will be receiving our attention in the coming year. Statistical tables and examples of incidents illustrating these and other safety issues are to be found in this report.

Beside the slam-door investigation, already mentioned, the Inspectorate was involved during the year in discussions with promoters and engineers of several major projects including the Channel Tunnel Rail Link, Crossrail, Docklands Light Railway Extension, East London Line Extension, Heathrow Express, Jubilee Line Extension and various light rapid transit schemes such as those at Croydon and Sheffield. Much of the work on these large-scale 'mega' projects is continuing with the great advantage that the Inspectorate is involved at each stage and is therefore aware of difficulties as they arise and is involved in the development of solutions. Often this work is innovatory and a challenge to conventional safety practices. Provided overall standards of safety are maintained a flexible response will always be given by the Inspectorate.

The Government issued a White Paper, *New opportunities for the railways - the privatisation of British Rail* (July 1992), and the Secretary of State asked the Health and Safety Commission to undertake a study of the safety implications. The result was a widely acclaimed report entitled *Ensuring safety on Britain's railways* which laid down the ground rules for those wishing to become railway operators. The Inspectorate participated extensively in this work. The Secretary of State for Transport accepted the report's 38 recommendations in full and the Inspectorate has been closely involved in the resulting development of new safety legislation.

Clearly, the changing regime on Britain's railways is going to cause the Inspectorate much additional work. The mega and other project work, coupled with the broadening of responsibilities for railway operation that will come with privatisation, create an urgent demand for up-to-date guidance on safety standards to be made available. In response the Inspectorate is reviewing the existing *Requirements* previously published by the Department of Transport with a view to publishing a revised and extended set of HSE documents in 1994.

I am pleased to report that the Secretary of State for Transport and the Health and Safety Executive have agreed to a significant increase in the Inspectorate staffing, and recruitment is already under way. New staff are being recruited, where possible, from the railways, but the opportunity is being taken to transfer-in expertise, for example on risk assessment, from other parts of HSE.

In the last annual report we promised to undertake research into the behaviour of road users at level crossings. This is now under way and will form part of a wider examination of level crossing hazards, on which we are working with BR. We are also co-sponsors of two further research projects. The first, co-sponsored with HSE's Local Authority Unit, is a study of the slip-resistance of flooring. Our interest in this subject stems from the problems experienced with terrazzo floor tiling in stations. Secondly, we are examining the validation of computer predictions of the development of fires in tunnels, co-sponsored with the Field Operations Division, the Technology and Health Sciences Division and the Offshore Safety Division, all of HSE. The results of all of the Inspectorate's research activities will feature in future annual reports.

It would appear that I am a recipient of the 'Chinese curse' because I have been appointed to my post at the start of 'interesting times'! I can only say that I view this prospect with excitement, but also with confidence, because I have had the good fortune to join a team of the most dedicated and competent staff. My thanks go to them for all the help they have given me to date and in particular for assembling this report.

Stanley Robertson
HM Chief Inspector of Railways

INTRODUCTION

Agency agreement

1 Her Majesty's Railway Inspectorate was transferred from the Department of Transport to the Health and Safety Executive on 1 December 1990. From that date a new agency agreement came into effect between the Health and Safety Commission and the Department of Transport requiring the Executive, on behalf of the Commission, to exercise certain functions on behalf of the Secretary of State by means of HM Railway Inspectorate.

2 Among these functions are the approval of new railway works, the making of level crossing orders, the publication of this report, the receipt of notices of accidents given under the Accident Reporting Order and certain duties under the Channel Tunnel Act 1987.

3 HM Chief Inspecting Officer of Railways as head of the Inspectorate has direct access to the Secretary of State to advise him on behalf of the Commission on matters arising out of or related to the performance of these functions.

4 The Commission provides the Secretary of State with information and advice in connection with these functions and on matters of safety and technical matters in relation to railways, tramways, underground and light railways or any other guided passenger transit systems.

Jurisdiction

5 There was no change during the period covered by this report in the jurisdiction of the Secretary of State for Transport under the regulatory acts affecting railway safety. These acts, and the procedures under which they are applied, are listed in Appendix 11. The report is based on accidents, failures and dangerous occurrences reported to the Secretary of State under the acts. The Transport and Works Act 1992, is a significant piece of legislation and is outlined in Appendix 11.

6 In addition to the railways of the British Railways Board, the main railway undertakings are the metropolitan railways: London Underground Limited, the Tyne & Wear Metro, Strathclyde Metropolitan Railway and the Docklands Light Railway. There are also some 230 minor railways which were either constructed with statutory authority or have a gauge in excess of 350 mm or both.

7 These railways are required to report to Her Majesty's Railway Inspectorate all notifiable accidents under railway or health and safety at work legislation. The accidents and failures are tabulated in Appendices 1 to 8. Supplementary statistics are shown tabulated in Tables 1 to 14 adjacent to the relevant text. There has been no change in the statutory reporting requirements since the publication of the annual report for 1991/92 although wrong side signalling failures (WSF) are reported by administrative arrangements. The Railways (Notice of Accidents) Order 1986 (SI No 2187) came into force on 1 January 1987 and the Reporting of Injuries, Diseases and Dangerous Occurrences Regulations 1985 (SI No 2023) on 1 April 1986.

Definitions

8 Accidents and failures are divided into four groups:

(a) *train accidents,* ie accidents to trains and rolling stock;

(b) *failures* of rolling stock, track and structures of a type which can cause train accidents;

(c) *movement accidents,* ie accidents to people caused by the movement of railway vehicles but excluding those involved in train accidents; and

(d) *non-movement accidents,* ie accidents to people on railway premises but not connected with the movement of railway vehicles.

9 Accidents to people are further subdivided into accidents to:

(a) passengers;

(b) railway staff including contractors' employees;

(c) other persons including people on business;

(d) occupants of road vehicles (ORV); and

(e) trespassers and suicides.

10 *Significant train accidents* are those that are actually or potentially most dangerous to passengers, whether or not they result in

casualties. These include most collisions and all derailments on or affecting passenger lines.

11 *Dangerous occurrences* are a class of incident defined in the Reporting of Injuries, Diseases and Dangerous Occurrences Regulations 1985 (RIDDOR). They are incidents likely to cause injury and must be reported under RIDDOR if no notifiable injury has actually occurred, unless otherwise notifiable under the Railways (Notice of Accidents) Order 1986.

Abbreviations

12 A list of abbreviations used in this report is given in Appendix 9.

Parameters of report

13 This report is based on the financial year 1 April 1992 to 31 March 1993. As BR had not completed its 'Organisation for Quality' (O for Q) reorganisation at the start of the year, the report will refer to regions rather than businesses.

Staff

14   February 1993 saw the retirement of Mr R J Seymour who had held the post of Chief Inspecting Officer since March 1988. His successor, Mr S S J Robertson, joined the Inspectorate from HSE's Field Operations Division where he was a Regional Director. Mr Robertson worked in the private sector before joining HM Factory Inspectorate in 1974. He is a member of the Council of the Institution of Electrical Engineers.

15   The Inspectorate continued to expand during 1992/93, with its overall strength increasing from 49 to 62. Successful recruiting campaigns attracted seven new Inspecting Officers and a Technical Officer to the Inspectorate, and there were two inward secondments from elsewhere in HSE to fill Principal Inspecting Officer and Inspecting Officer posts. An Inspecting Officer was loaned to HSE's Safety Policy Division to assist with the development of proposals for post-privatisation safety regulation on the railways.

16   At 31 March 1993, the professional staff in post comprised the Chief and Deputy Chief Inspecting Officers, three Assistant Chief Inspecting Officers, 12 Principal Inspecting Officers, 18 Inspecting Officers and two Technical Officers. During the year, the administration and secretarial staff rose commensurately to 25.

Principal accident inquiries

17   No inquiries under the powers of the Regulation of Railways Act 1871 were held during the period.

Approval of new works

18   This section covers the inspections referred to in Appendix 11. New works include: new passenger lines; new stations; electrifications; significant resignalling of lines; and significant track and station works on the existing railway. Modernization of level crossings, work on minor railways, the Channel Tunnel and railways overseas are dealt with elsewhere in this report.

19   The 'approvals' workload held steady during the year and numerous larger schemes continued to be submitted. The backlog of schemes, however, was reduced to the stage where, at various times during the year, the only outstanding items rested with the railways, who had been asked to clarify various matters. The Inspectorate's policy of inspecting all major works and a sample of minor works was maintained with a total of 79 inspections during the year, of which 58 were carried out by inspecting officers located in area offices. One-hundred-and-ten new bridges and 125 other works schemes received approval.

Staff training - Inspectorate administrative staff on railway familiarisation.

20 Recent annual reports have expressed concern that many minor works schemes are not being submitted. Despite the hope expressed in last year's report, the situation has not improved. Although members of the Inspectorate have made presentations to BR project managers on the statutory requirements of the Road and Rail Traffic Act 1933, the general level of awareness of project managers still remains low. With the forthcoming introduction of Regulations made under the Transport and Works Act 1992, replacing the 1933 Act, it is to be hoped that BR will make a determined effort to ensure that its staff are aware of the statutory requirements they contain. It is envisaged that much of the revised Requirements will be published at about the same time as the Regulations.

21 Late submission of schemes has remained a problem. In one case, information on very restricted clearances was not supplied until three weeks after the originally proposed date for taking the works into use. In another, the works were taken into use in an unsafe condition, at the same time as the submission was made. Only rapid action by the division concerned in bringing the works up to a temporarily tolerable condition, avoided the need for the Inspectorate to take enforcement action. In one case of a relocated station, the works were taken into use without the Secretary of State's approval and criminal proceedings were considered.

22 In last year's report, comments were made about schemes offered for inspection during 1990 before they were complete, although it was noted that there had been no difficulties in 1991/92. Unfortunately, the problem has reappeared and continued beyond this reporting year. The worst case involved the re-opening of the Maesteg (WR) branch to passenger traffic when HMRI received two assurances in writing from the project manager that the signalling was ready for inspection. On arrival, it was found that the power supplies were not available for the signalling.

23 Certain signalling submissions, although theoretically sound, would have led to unsatisfactory situations. In one case, it was possible for two passenger trains to face each other on a single line, either side of a ground frame. In another, the poor positioning of three-aspect colour-light signals would have meant the train driver travelling excessive distances between caution and stop aspects. There was also a tendency for signalling schemes involving bi-directional working to be completed well in advance of the associated staff safety work, such as the provision of clear cesses. In these cases approval was only given for right-direction running pending completion of the work.

24 Following the publication of the report into the accident at *Newton (ScR)*, the embargo placed on single-lead junctions was lifted. In accordance with the recommendations of the report, risk assessments were requested in respect of the *Cowlairs* curve *(ScR)*, *Latchmere Junction (SR)* and the *West London Line* and part of the *Paddington* remodelling *(WR)*.

25 The restrictions on the use of axle counters remained, pending the outcome of the inquiry into the accident in the *Severn Tunnel (WR)*.

26 There were many small projects completed during 1992/93, but few notable schemes. Amongst these were:

(a) the electrification of the line from *Cambridge* to *Kings Lynn (AR)*;

(b) the rebuilding and refurbishment of *East Croydon Station (SR)*, eliminating what had become a notorious eyesore. The station, a modern steel and glass design, has well over 500 train departures daily;

(c) the re-opening of the line from *Bridgend* to *Maesteg (WR)* to passengers, together with the provision of several new halts; and

(d) reconstruction of *Angel Station (LUL)*. (See Chapter 8.)

27 Additionally, important elements of continuing major projects received approval, including:

(a) the electrification of the line between *Aston* and *Lichfield (LMR)*, part of the Cross-City route in the West Midlands; and

(b) the electrification of the *West London Line*, new spur lines at *Chislehurst (SR)* and the provision of additional platforms at *Orpington (SR)* as part of the preparation and upgrading of the routes from London to the Channel Tunnel for international traffic.

Level crossing modernization

28 It was stated in last year's report that British Railways intended to replace all 44 automatic open crossings remotely monitored (AOCR) following the report produced by Professor Stott* and that it was anticipated that the replacement programme would be completed during 1992. Of the three shown remaining at 31 March 1993, *Naas (WR)*, near Ledbury, Gloucestershire, was completed in mid-1993 shortly after the end of the year under review. *Bulcote (ER)*, near Nottingham, has been deferred because BR wish to incorporate the controls for its protection into a proposed larger resignalling scheme which has been delayed because of a shortage of skilled manpower. Even where AOCR comply with the Stott criteria, BR made the decision to phase out all AOCR in due course. However, even though it falls into this category, *Rosarie (ScR)*, near Wick, Highland Region, is being deferred indefinitely with the agreement of HMRI because of its low rail and road usage.

29 Of the 39 automatic open crossings locally monitored (AOCL) that also failed to meet the criteria specified in the Stott Report, improvements to the protection of 31 had been completed by the end of March 1993, 12 having been completed during the previous twelve months.

30 The programme of modernization of level crossings has continued, albeit at a slower pace than in previous years. Twenty-eight inspections of modernized crossings were carried out during the year 1992/93 compared with 37 last year and 68 during the calender year 1990. The reduction in numbers is attributed to the shortage of skilled signal-testing staff and the additional tasks placed upon them to meet the recommendations of the Clapham Junction accident report. Preparatory work is nevertheless continuing on the modernization of level crossings and 37 consultation meetings with county council and local authority representatives were undertaken. In addition, there were 151 submissions by the railways making major amendments to the protection laid down in statutory orders and 101 minor amendments.

31 Accidents at unprotected footpath crossings are a major source of fatalities to members of the general public. The only criterion by which the railways are bound regarding footpaths has been imposed by the line of the public footpath that existed before the railway was constructed. The railway's statutory duty at these crossings is to provide gates or stiles and convenient approaches. The standard 'Stop, Look, Listen, Beware of Trains' signs must be displayed. Because of the increase in train speeds and the comparative silence of their approach, HSE issued, on behalf of the Department of Transport, a supplement to the Requirements** dealing with the protection of footpath and bridleway level crossings. Published in January 1993, it includes parameters for sighting times, crossing surfaces and the need for additional protection.

Health and safety at work

32 The inspectors in the field are the eyes and ears of the Inspectorate in assessing safety standards at working level. They provide advice or, where necessary, take more formal action to promote and maintain adequate standards of safety, and provide intelligence to HQ both regarding trends and serious isolated incidents.

33 The number of field inspectors has continued to grow, although during the year under review, and subsequently, they have been increasingly involved in special projects to assist in the development of safety policy and enforcement strategy. By the end of March 1993 a total of six Principal Inspecting Officers, directly or indirectly involved in field operations, were supported by 18 Inspecting Officers. Of this total only three had been in the Inspectorate five years earlier.

34 A need has been identified for more resources to manage this larger field force effectively, to guide and co-ordinate efforts and to liaise with other branches of HSE over policy and operational matters. In the interim a Principal Inspector has been seconded from another division of HSE to assist the head of branch; further increases in management posts are proposed.

35 This year the field inspectors were not so heavily involved with major accident investigations as in the previous year but their remit continued to be widened. Additional tasks included new works and minor railways inspections which hitherto had usually been dealt with by headquarters-based inspectors. Traditional inspection and advisory duties remained at a high level but the Inspectorate's

* *Automatic open level crossings: a review of safety* HMSO 1987 ISBN 0 11 550831 7

** *Protection of footpath and bridleway level crossings* Railway Construction and Operation Requirements Part F, Section 18, HMSO 1993 ISBN 0 11 882115 6

preparedness to use more formal powers when it is considered appropriate was reflected in the serving of 17 enforcement notices and the hearing of eight prosecutions relating to unsafe conditions on the railway, some of which related to the actions of contractors, not involving the running of trains.

36 There are some encouraging signs that health and safety at work is receiving more appropriate attention - the subject of safety is so high on the agenda of discussions that some speak of 'saturation' with safety issues. Despite this effort the railway at working level still has far to go to eliminate unsafe actions and make rigorously safe conduct the normal way of working. Perceptions of personal risk are not high enough compared to issues of personal convenience and work-output goals.

Automatic train protection

37 During the year, further work was undertaken by British Railways on the testing and evaluation of the two Automatic Train Protection (ATP) pilot schemes. Delays in this important safety project have continued and British Railways had not made sufficient progress to be able to discuss with the Inspectorate the results of the pilot schemes or the strategy for installation of ATP. These subjects are being studied by consultants on behalf of BR.

Channel Tunnel

38 The delays in the construction of the Channel Tunnel have been frequently documented elsewhere. As a result, the hand-over of site-safety responsibility from our HSE colleagues in the Field Operations Division to HMRI has not yet been completed. However, the delays have not reduced the extensive workload of those members of the Inspectorate directly involved with the scheme. The Deputy Chief Inspecting Officer has continued as a member of the Inter-Governmental Safety Authority and as Chairman of the Rail Working Group. He has been supported in this by an Assistant Chief Inspecting Officer, who acts as his deputy, and a Principal Inspecting Officer with specialist knowledge of signalling, control and communications.

39 The heavy demands placed on these members of the Inspectorate are likely to continue for some time. This team is supported by other members of the Inspectorate and other HSE inspectors.

'Table Top' exercises - the Inspectorate and British Transport Police jointly assist in conducting incident management courses.

A variety of warning lights demonstrated to the Inspectorate by BR.

Other activities

40   Through the Deputy Chief Inspecting
Officer, the Inspectorate has continued to
provide advice to the Hong Kong Government
on the safety of their various railway systems.
During the course of the year advice was
sought on the railway which is to be part of a
new airport proposal.

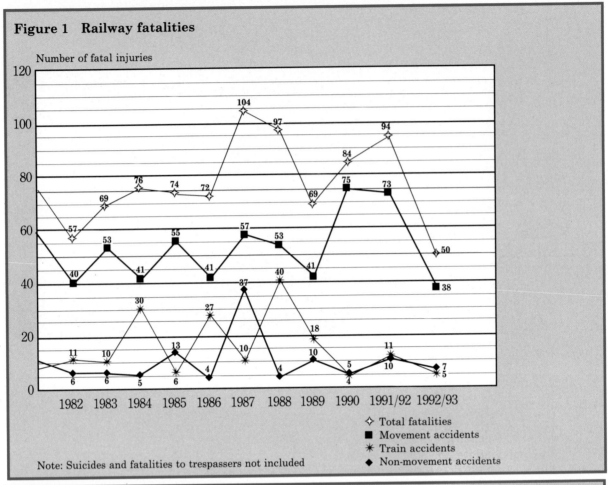

Figure 1 Railway fatalities

Number of fatal injuries

Legend:
◇ Total fatalities
■ Movement accidents
✳ Train accidents
◆ Non-movement accidents

Note: Suicides and fatalities to trespassers not included

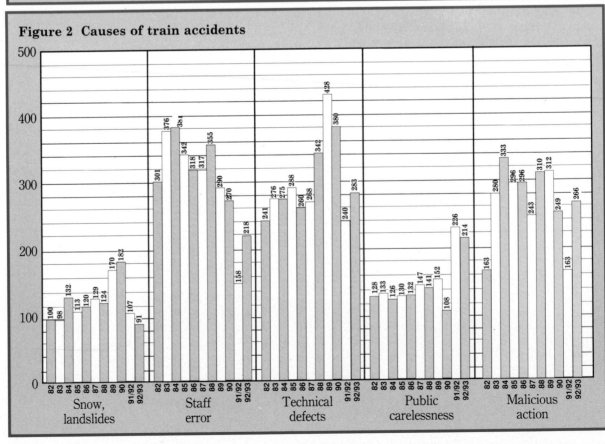

Figure 2 Causes of train accidents

Snow, landslides · Staff error · Technical defects · Public carelessness · Malicious action

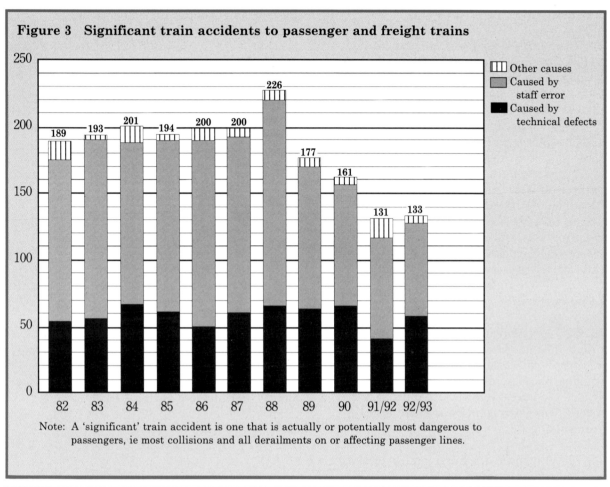

Figure 3 Significant train accidents to passenger and freight trains

Other causes
Caused by staff error
Caused by technical defects

189 193 201 194 200 200 226 177 161 131 133

82 83 84 85 86 87 88 89 90 91/92 92/93

Note: A 'significant' train accident is one that is actually or potentially most dangerous to
passengers, ie most collisions and all derailments on or affecting passenger lines.

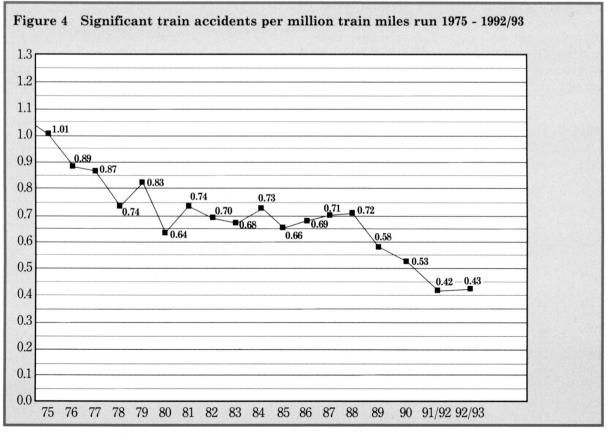

Figure 4 Significant train accidents per million train miles run 1975 - 1992/93

1.01 0.89 0.87 0.74 0.83 0.64 0.74 0.70 0.68 0.73 0.66 0.69 0.71 0.72 0.58 0.53 0.42 0.43

75 76 77 78 79 80 81 82 83 84 85 86 87 88 89 90 91/92 92/93

Accident rates

41 Train and movement accidents are related to billions of passenger miles. Non-movement accidents are shown per billion passenger journeys as that figure relates more closely to the use of stations.

42 The figures in Table 1 are derived from those shown in Appendix 1 which relate to operating statistics, and from Appendix 2, the analysis of fatal, major and minor injuries sustained on the railways of Great Britain during 1992/93. Except where otherwise specified, the term 'railways' includes tramways, the metropolitan railways and minor railways (eg preserved lines).

Fatal accidents

43 Excluding suicides and trespassers, 50 people died on the railways in 1992/93 in all accidents. Of these, 28 were passengers, of whom all but two died in movement accidents. This is the lowest number of fatalities on record. No passengers were killed in train accidents.

44 Eleven railway staff and contractors' staff lost their lives during 1992/93, which is the lowest annual figure ever. The previous lowest annual tolls were in the years 1986-88, with 16 lives being lost each year. Ten years ago, the number killed was 27; this progressive improvement is encouraging. (See Chapter 10 for more details.)

45 Eleven people in the category 'other persons' were killed. They were nearly all users of level crossings. (See Chapter 4 for more details.)

Train accidents

46 Although, sadly, a driver was killed in a collision between freight trains, it is very gratifying to be able to report that no passengers were killed in train accidents during the year 1992/93. This is the seventh 'clear' year in the last twenty, so far as passengers are concerned. Furthermore, only three passengers were seriously injured, which represents a remarkable improvement over the average of 27 during the previous ten years. On BR there were only six collisions and 11 derailments in which passenger trains were involved, and all of these were at relatively low speed.

All collisions and derailments

47 Casualties resulting from the 154 collisions and 205 derailments during 1992/93 were as follows:

	Passengers	Staff
Fatal	Nil	1
Major injury	2	2
Minor injury	45	24

Table 1 Death or injury risk to passengers

Year	Train accidents per billion passenger miles			Movement accidents per billion passenger miles			Non-movement accidents per billion passenger journeys		
	Killed	Major	Minor	Killed	Major	Minor	Killed	Major	Minor
1987	0.12	0.53	12.17	1.47	3.28	106.90	18.82	54.51	2314
1988	1.33	2.94	21.17	1.33	4.00	102.70	0.61	81.13	2399
1989	0.24	1.58	11.03	1.01	3.93	105.40	1.25	82.55	2687
1990	0.00	0.53	5.88	1.51	4.37	104.10	1.29	67.31	2293
1991/92	0.08	0.75	12.01	2.20	3.03	90.65	1.89	63.64	2091
1992/93	0.00	0.13	2.67	1.10	3.35	99.00	1.29	100.26	2395

Movement accidents

48 Movement accidents are those which befall people due to the movement of trains but do not include train accidents. For example, passengers injured when boarding or alighting from moving trains and those struck by trains when standing too close to the edge of the platform are included.

49 In 1992/93, 26 passengers and five staff were killed in movement accidents, which represents an improvement over the previous year, when 53 passengers and nine staff were killed. Details of accidents to staff are dealt with in Chapter 10.

50 Eight passengers were killed in the year 1992/93 by falling off platforms and being struck or run over by trains, compared with 16 for 1991/92 and an annual average of five during the years 1985-90. There are no indications of any underlying worsening of the situation; the difficulty lies in classifying the casualty (see paragraph 60).

51 The same situation applies to the figure of six passengers being killed while crossing the line at stations. The problem first emerged last year when 15 deaths were recorded from this cause. The scale of the statistical anomaly may be gathered from the fact that only two deaths were recorded from this cause during the whole of the six years 1985-90. Reference was made to this problem in paragraph 317 of last year's annual report.

52 Nine passengers died as a result of falling from trains with slam doors, an improvement over the figure of 19 for each of the last four years. As reported last year, this subject was thoroughly investigated by HSE and a report has been published by HMSO, entitled *Passenger falls from train doors* (ISBN 0 11 882125 3). The investigation showed that a door which is securely fastened with the lock properly engaged will not open in transit. However, the investigation also established the existence of failure modes affecting locks and the fit of train doors into their frames which could lead to closed doors opening

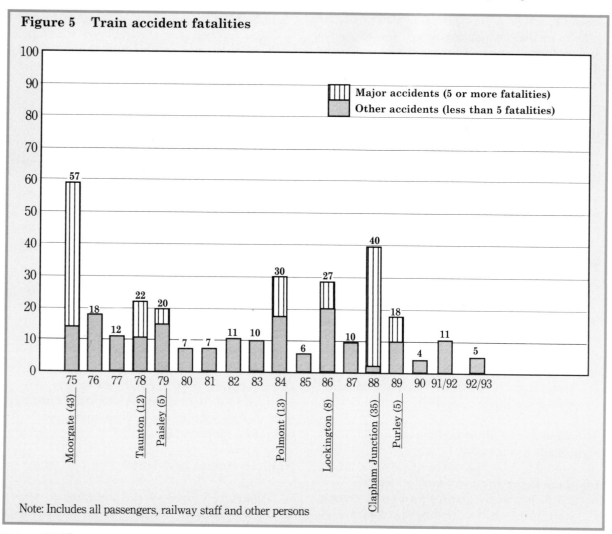

Figure 5   Train accident fatalities

Note: Includes all passengers, railway staff and other persons

Slam doors - an HST at London, St Pancras.

unexpectedly if pressure was applied with the train in motion. The report was also critical of aspects of BR's management, and installation and maintenance procedures. However, during the investigation no incident involving death or injury could be attributed to a door not being properly closed. The investigation confirmed that most of the incidents investigated show that alcohol or misbehaviour was a factor to one degree or another.

53 In response to the HSE report, BR has announced that it has embarked on the following measures to reduce the scale of the problem even further:

(a) fitting new one-piece primary locks to InterCity coaches, to be completed within 12 months;

(b) fitting secondary locking systems, operated by the guard, on InterCity coaches, over the next two years; and

(c) designing a new primary lock and locking system for other slam-door coaches.

54 A number of other factors are also significant in that now:

(a) there is better supervision on station platforms, and a greater awareness among staff of the need to ensure that doors are properly closed before departure;

(b) passengers are more aware of the dangers of leaning on doors and playing with the handles, thanks to the publicity which has been given to the subject by the press and television, and the warning announcements now given on trains;

(c) there are improved maintenance methods and control; and

(d) life-expired slam-door stock is continuously being withdrawn and replaced by stock equipped with power-operated doors under the control of the traincrew.

55 Three passengers were killed and 34 received major injuries when joining or alighting from trains, or when attempting to do so. These are classed as movement accidents because they were accidents to people, rather than casualties arising from accidents to trains. Most result from hurried or thoughtless actions when doors are under passenger control. However, in an unusual accident at *Hounslow East Station (LUL)* an elderly lady received fatal injuries when alighting after her coat was trapped in the sliding doors (see Chapter 8 for details).

Non-movement accidents

56 Appendix 7 analyses the statistics of those accidents which do not involve the movement of trains.

57 Seven people were killed in non-movement accidents in 1992/93, compared with ten the previous year. Two were passengers and five were staff. Staff fatalities are dealt with in detail in Chapter 10.

Trespassers and suicides

58 See Appendix 8 for analysis.

59 A total of 224 trespassers, including suicides, were killed by trains. The figure of 122 trespassers is somewhat lower than the average of 148 for the previous five years, but the recorded number of suicides has shown a considerable and inexplicable reduction over recent years, as shown below.

Year	Number of suicides recorded
1987	169
1988	154
1989	137
1990	113
1991/92	112
1992/93	102

60 When a body is found on or near a railway line it is often difficult to determine whether the person was a passenger or a trespasser and whether their death was accidental or the result of suicide. The classifications and figures used in this report are based on the decisions of coroners' courts.

61 The total number of children under the age of 16 who were killed while trespassing was five.

62 The difficulty, in practice, of preventing determined youngsters from trespassing on the railway was well illustrated in an accident near *Loughborough Junction (NSE)*, Greater London, when a 14-year-old boy was killed. In order to gain access to the line the boy had to climb ten feet on to a garage roof, then through a barbed wire entanglement on to a sloping roof against the side of the railway viaduct. From this point he had to climb on to a metal grille in order to get within reach of the railings on the viaduct parapet.

63 Two 17-year-old youths were killed when they were struck by a train while they were riding a motor cycle along the railway track near *Mirfield (ER)*, West Yorkshire, shortly before 5 pm, on *23 November 1992*. The Coroner's jury returned a verdict of misadventure.

General

64   There were 1152 train accidents in 1992/93, but the great majority were of a minor nature. This is an apparent increase over the previous year's figure of 960, but is mainly accounted for by an increase in accidents under the heading 'Trains running into other obstacles' (Index 9(c), Appendix 3), from 190 in 1991/92 to 387 in 1992/93. It is probable that there was a degree of under-reporting in 1991/92, because the annual average during the five years 1986-90 was well over 300.

65   The annual average number of train accidents reported during the five years 1986-90 was 1276, therefore the result for 1992/93 is not out of line, and in fact shows some reduction. The figure for 1991/92 must therefore be treated with some reservations.

66   As in previous years, technical defects caused more train accidents (283, 25%) than staff error (218, 19%). Other causes accounted for the remaining 651 train accidents (56%), among which were:

Animals on the line	51	(4%)
Irregular opening of doors	136	(12%)
Malicious acts of the public	266	(23%)

67   A more accurate measure of the risk to passengers is given by the number of accidents which are classified as significant. These include collisions involving passenger trains, derailments of passenger trains, collisions and derailments of freight trains on passenger lines, and trains running into buffer stops at stations.

68   There were 133 significant train accidents in 1992/93, the figure for the previous year being 131. However, the current year's results show a considerable improvement over the five years 1986-90, for which the annual average was 193.

69   Freight train derailments and collisions on passenger lines are considered significant owing to the risk of a passenger train running into the wreckage. However, no passenger train struck such an obstruction in 1992/93.

70   Passenger train mileage on BR and the metropolitan railways in 1992/93 was 274 million (BR 228 million, metropolitan railways 46 million). This is an increase of 15 million over 1991/92. The annual average for the five years 1986-90 was 248 million (BR 213 million, metropolitan railways 35 million). Passenger train mileage on the railways of Great Britain has been growing fairly consistently, year by year, and is now 17% greater than it was five years ago.

Table 2   Significant train accidents

Collisions involving passenger trains
                    7 (6 on BR)

Trains running into the buffers at stations
                    25 (23 on BR)

Derailments of passenger trains
                    30 (11 on BR)

Collisions and derailments of freight trains
on passenger lines   71 (62 on BR)

Accident inquiries

71   No public inquiries into accidents were initiated during 1992/93. This is believed to be the first year in the history of the Railway Inspectorate in which there were no accidents that were judged to be sufficiently serious to warrant the holding of a public inquiry.

Table 3   Train accident public inquiry and investigation reports published since 1991/92

Date of accident	Description and reference
12 August 1987	Collision of a passenger train with the buffer-stops at *Walton-on-Naze (AR)* HMSO 1992 ISBN 0 11 882086 9 Price £5.00
20 April 1989	Collision between a light locomotive and a freight train at *Holton Heath (SR)* HMSO 1993 ISBN 0 11 882072 9 Price £5.00
21 July 1991	Collision between two passenger trains at *Newton Junction (ScR)* HMSO 1992 ISBN 0 11 882054 0 Price £10.00

Collisions

Collisions between passenger trains

72 Six collisions between passenger trains were reported in 1992/93. They were all at relatively low speed, causing no deaths and only two major injuries. Two of the more interesting were as follows:

(a) at *Holbeck (ER)*, near Leeds, Yorkshire, on *22 May 1992*, a head-on collision occurred between the 20.30 King's Cross to Leeds express and the 22.52 Leeds to Sheffield Sprinter. A lineside fire had damaged the signalling cables, causing a major signalling failure, and trains were being handsignalled. The staff on the ground made an error concerning the lie of the points, causing the express to be switched to the wrong line and into collision with the Sprinter unit. Four passengers were detained in hospital overnight. At a hearing in Bradford Crown Court, BR pleaded guilty to two charges of endangering the safety of passengers and staff, and was fined £25 000 for endangering the safety of the public and £25 000 for endangering the safety of its employees.

(b) at *London Bridge (NSE)*, during the early morning of *25 November 1992*, when the driver of a Charing Cross to Tunbridge Wells train, formed of Class 411 electric multiple units, wrongly passed a signal at danger. It came into sidelong collision, at a speed of approximately 15 mile/h, with a similarly-formed train from Ramsgate to Charing Cross, travelling at about 10 mile/h. This resulted in two passengers receiving major injuries (one man with cracked ribs and one knocked unconscious with bruising and cuts to the head), and 17 minor injuries (mainly cuts, bruises and shock).

Collisions between passenger trains and freight trains or light locomotives

73 Only one accident was reported under this heading, which occurred at very low speed. There were no injuries.

Collisions between freight trains, light locomotives or other moving vehicles

74 Of the 11 collisions in this category, only three were classified as significant, having occurred on passenger lines.

75 A collision which resulted in the death of the driver of a freight train occurred near *Morpeth (ER)* near Northumberland on *13 November 1992*. Vandalism had damaged the cables and optic fibres conveying indications from a level crossing to a signal box. This meant that trains were having to be authorised to pass the signal at Danger. A freight train protecting the crossing stopped at the signal and because of the damage the driver had to go some distance to find a telephone that would work. Meanwhile a second freight train drew up at the signal behind the first train. The driver of the second train went to the telephone and because he and the signalman failed to identify his train and the signal from which he was speaking the signalman authorised him to pass the signal at Danger assuming that he was the driver of the first train. The driver of the second train set off and collided violently with the rear of the standing train.

76 A typical accident occurred at *Liverpool Lime Street Station (LMR)*, on *28 December 1992*, during a shunting movement from one platform to another. During the movement the signalman decided to change the platform into which the shunt was to be made, but this information did not reach the shunter or the driver, who were expecting to enter an empty platform. Instead, they were diverted into another platform where they collided with empty coaching stock. The driver and shunter were also at fault regarding the manning of the locomotive.

77 Several of the collisions occurred during engineers' possessions of the line. Such collisions, and the casualties which often result from them, have been a recurring problem for many years, and it has proved extremely difficult to devise procedures and safety equipment (lamps, signs, radio, etc) that would provide adequate safety during such operations. Considerable efforts have been made to improve the situation, with some success, but there is still some way to go, and a determined effort needs to be made to produce a realistic and practical solution.

78 The planned duration of engineering possessions tends to be constrained by the demands of the passenger timetable, and the insistence that the possession be given up at the due time. The inevitable result is that the work is carried out with one eye on the clock, the consequences of which are not always conducive to safety.

Collisions between trains and buffer stops

79 There were 25 such accidents in 1992/93, compared with a yearly average of 42 during the previous five years. The attention given to the subject following the fatal collision at *Cannon Street (NSE)*, London, on *8 January 1991*, appears to have had good effect. Not all of the trains concerned were carrying passengers, and most of the impacts were at low speed. There were no major injuries.

80 However, there was a buffer stop collision at the relatively high reported speed of 25 mile/h at *Balloch (ScR)*, Strathclyde, on *25 March 1993*. The train concerned was a Class 320 EMU but fortunately it was conveying only four passengers at that stage of its journey and none was injured. The driver misjudged his braking.

81 A rather more serious incident occurred at *Springburn (ScR)*, Glasgow, on *3 February 1993*, involving the same type of unit. A train from Milngavie collided with an empty Class 320 EMU which was standing in the platform, resulting in minor injuries to four passengers and five traincrew. The incoming train should have stopped short of the train already in the platform, then subsequently coupled to it for the return journey. The cause of the accident was an error by the driver.

82 Oil and grease on the railhead caused a Class 108 diesel multiple unit (DMU) to collide heavily with the buffers at *Bristol Temple Meads (WR)*, on *11 August 1992*. When the driver applied the brakes the wheels locked and the train skidded. A party of six adults and 33 children were travelling on the train and, as is almost always the case, they were standing, preparing to alight, when the impact occurred. Several suffered minor injuries.

Derailments

Derailments of passenger trains

83 Thirty passenger train derailments were reported in 1992/93, which is very much in line with previous years. However, only eleven of these occurred on BR lines (down from 13 in 1991/92 and 23 in 1990), with two on LUL and no fewer than 17 on other railways or on tramways (see Chapter 7 for details). Almost all of the derailments occurred at low speed with no serious injuries. The incidents which occurred on LUL and other railways are dealt with in the appropriate chapters.

84 The faulty condition of the permanent way is a common cause of derailment, examples being:

(a) between *Effingham Junction* and *Bookham (NSE)*, Surrey, on *21 May 1992*, a Class 319 Thameslink train had one bogie derailed as a result of track twist and gauge widening;

(b) one bogie of a Class 165 DMU from Slough was derailed at 23 mile/h on the curve leading into *Windsor Station (NSE)*, Berkshire, on *11 February 1993*, by a combination of sidewear of the high rail, track twist and lateral misalignment. There were no injuries. The speed at the time of derailment was provided accurately by the on-train data recorder;

(c) *Culgaith (LMR)*, Cumbria, on the line between Settle and Carlisle, is an area prone to landslips, and derailments have occurred there in the past. Another took place on *2 December 1992*, derailing the Class 156 Sprinter DMU on a Carlisle-Leeds service. One passenger suffered a whiplash injury.

85 Driver error is also a common cause of derailment. One such incident occurred at *Waterloo (NSE)*, London, on *23 January 1993*. The driver of a departing train passed a signal at Danger and proceeded on to the wrong line, on which an incoming train was approaching. Fortunately, both drivers realised what was happening in sufficient time to bring their trains to a stand, thus avoiding what might have been a serious head-on collision. The driver of the departing train then set back, but one pair of wheels became derailed because the points were not correctly set for the movement, having just been run through. There was some confusion between the signalman and the traincrew about the movement.

86 In another case, at *Sydney Bridge Junction, Crewe (LMR)*, Cheshire, on *12 November 1992*, a Class 158 Sprinter Express DMU became derailed on pointwork when the driver passed a signal at Danger. He was the only casualty, and suffered shock.

Derailments of freight trains

87 One-hundred-and-seventy-five freight train derailments were reported in 1992/93, of which 68 were regarded as significant. This is in line with previous years, except for 1991/92, when only 121 freight train derailments were reported.

88 The figures for freight train derailments in previous years, as reported, were:

  1990 157, including 76 significant (48%)

  1989 160, including 60 significant (38%)

  1988 203, including 112 significant (55%)

  1987 172, including 116 significant (67%)

  1986 158, including 99 significant (63%)

89 Defective track is a common cause of freight train derailments, some examples follow:

(a) a train of roadstone from Mountsorrel to Didcot, conveying 29 privately-owned hopper wagons, had its fifth wagon from the locomotive derailed at *Dorridge (LMR)*, West Midlands, near Solihull, on *6 February 1993*. The Research Department were called in from Derby to assist in the investigation, and it was concluded that wet spots on the cess side of the track, leading to a dip, were the cause of the derailment;

(b) a similar load was being conveyed on a train from *Rylstone (LMR)*, near Skipton, North Yorkshire to Hull, when eight wagons were derailed near the starting point on *26 January 1993.* Five of the wagons fell down an embankment. Derby Research Department again assisted in establishing the cause, which was track spread owing to deterioration of sleepers. This single line exists only to serve a quarry, which has recently received a grant for increased traffic by rail;

(c) the term 'freight trains' includes empty coaching stock trains. An empty coaching stock train, composed of a Class 455 EMU and a Class 456 EMU, travelling from Selhurst Depot to *London Victoria (NSE)*, on *19 October 1992,* was derailed at Victoria due to a combination of track twist and rail side-wear. Two coaches were derailed, and a further one turned over on to its side. There were no injuries. BR's Derby Research Deparment were also called in to assist at this derailment.

These three examples illustrate the reliance placed by BR operators and technical staff upon the expertise of the Research Department.

90 Not all derailments are the responsibility of the civil engineer, but his track always suffers from the consequences. In a derailment at *Otterington (ER)*, near Thirsk, North Yorkshire, on *13 May 1992,* the twenty-first wagon (an empty 'merry-go-round' coal hopper) in a freight train travelling from York to Seaham became completely derailed and buffer-locked with the adjacent vehicles. The train continued on its way for a further two miles, damaging a large number of sleepers and track fastenings. The derailment was caused by mechanical failure of the disc brake bolts, resulting in excessive out-of-balance forces and cyclic unloading of a leading wheel.

91 Defective track of all types caused 76 derailments in 1992/93, which continues a rising trend that became evident during the later 1980s. The annual average from 1982 to 1987 was only 34. Further investigation is to be made into this situation, which is clearly unsatisfactory.

Staff error

92 For many years, irregular block working by signalmen has been an infrequent cause of accident. There was no case in 1992/93.

93 Eleven accidents, including two collisions and seven derailments, were caused by drivers passing signals at danger. This subject is dealt with more fully in Chapter 6, Failures.

Other causes

94 The number of reported instances in which trains ran into animals on the line was 112, which is similar to the figure for previous years. While the majority of the instances concern sheep, which cause little or no hazard to trains, they have to be reported where the train is disabled (usually due to damage to the brake pipes). Cattle are a different matter, and the potential for a serious derailment following a collision with cattle is ever-present. The accident at *Polmont (ScR)*, on *30 July 1984,* in which 13 passengers were killed, is a stark example. Two typical cases were:

(a) a train from Hull to Scarborough, formed by a Class 156 Sprinter DMU, struck a cow between *Beverley* and *Driffield (ER)*, East Yorkshire, on *20 August 1992,* while the train was travelling at 70 mile/h. The train was not derailed but was extensively damaged and had to be taken out of service. No one was injured.

(b) the same class of unit was involved in a similar collision at *Eckington (WR)*, between Worcester and Cheltenham, on *2 December 1992*. The train was travelling at 75 mile/h and was momentarily lifted off the track by the impact, but fortunately was not derailed. The train was damaged, but was able to move forward to Cheltenham at 5 mile/h after a delay of $1\frac{1}{2}$ hours. There was no injury to passengers or crew.

95 Multiple units are particularly vulnerable to derailment following collisions with cattle, and continuing attention needs to be given to the adequate maintenance of lineside fencing.

96 Three-hundred-and-eighty-seven reports were received of trains running into 'other obstacles' (ie excluding vehicles at level crossings and animals). This heading accounts for almost exactly a third of all train accidents listed in Appendix 3. The figure is in line with previous years except for 1991/92, when there were only 190 reports.

97 Vandalism, in the form of placing obstructions on the line, is an ever-present source of concern. Examples are as follows:

(a) at *Trowell Junction (LMR)*, near Nottingham, on *24 February 1993,* a Class 158 Sprinter Express DMU on a cross-country service ran into a slab of concrete;

(b) at *Soho Road (LMR)*,Birmingham, on *23 March 1993,* a Class 150 DMU, running empty at 45 mile/h, was derailed when it struck a piece of rail on the track. The driver suffered shock and bruising;

(c) at *Coulsdon South (NSE)*, Surrey, on *10 January 1993,* a Gatwick Express train, travelling at 75 mile/h, struck a number of articles on the track, but was stopped safely. The articles included a mile post, a platform seat and a litter bin. The divisional director offered a reward of £2000 for information regarding those responsible for the incident which regrettably he has not had to pay;

(d) at *Burnley (LMR)*, Lancashire, on *10 August 1992,* a Class 142 Pacer unit ran into concrete troughing and was disabled. While the troughing was being removed, youths were seen placing more troughing on the line only 100 yards away. A similar attack was made at Brierfield, only two miles away, nine days later.

98 In each case, the British Transport Police carry out investigations, but only occasionally do they succeed in apprehending the culprits. The difficulties the police face in such circumstances are obvious, and while patrols may be stepped up in the areas concerned, the police do not have the manpower to carry out such operations on a national basis indefinitely. In some of the cases the culprits are under the age of criminal responsibility. For many years the police and railway staff, especially drivers, have visited schools to explain to children the dangers of trespass, and obstructing the line, and BR has made two new films for showing in schools.

99 Civil engineers have made great efforts to reduce the amount of material lying at the trackside, and to reduce the time during which material for maintenance and renewals is left on site before and after work periods, in order to limit its availability to vandals. However, concrete troughing, used by the signal engineer, is a material which is often used by vandals, and consideration has been given to means of reducing the potential risk from this source. The lightweight plastic material used as a replacement in some areas was not sufficiently robust.

100 Vandalism not only takes the form of placing obstacles on the track, as the following examples show:

(a) while an empty car-carrying train was standing at a signal at *Lifford East Junction (LMR)*, Birmingham, on *24 February 1993,* vandals uncoupled the train;

(b) a heavy object was thrown from a bridge on to the overhead line equipment (OLE) at *Halewood (LMR)*, Liverpool on *16 May 1992,* which caused it to sag. A diesel-hauled express came into contact with the OLE, smashing the windscreen of the locomotive.

101 The situation known as 'bridge-bashing' is dealt with in Chapter 6. In one case at *Allervale (WR)*, near Newton Abbott, Devon, on *11 December 1992,* a lorry skidded into the parapet of a bridge over the railway and caused debris to fall on to the track. This was run into by a Class 158 Sprinter Express DMU, causing some damage to the train. Notice of liability was served on the owners of the lorry.

102 Road vehicles occasionally run off the road on to an adjacent parallel railway line. Such a case occurred on *1 April 1992*, at *Hatfield Peverel (AR)*, near Chelmsford, when a car ran

Table 4   Significant collisions

Year	Total	Between passenger trains	Between passenger and other trains	Between non-passenger trains	With buffer stops
1987	64	6	14	11	33
1988	86	8	10	16	52
1989	85	12	11	7	55
1990	59	4	10	4	41
1991/92	52	10	3	8	31
Average 1987 to 1991/92	69	8	10	9	42
1992/93	35	6	1	3	25

(Averages are rounded to nearest whole number)

Table 5   Significant derailments

Year	Total	Passenger trains	Non-passenger trains	*Basic causes*		
				Staff error	Technical defects	Other causes
1987	136	20	116	72	56	8
1988	140	28	112	64	71	5
1989	92	32	60	28	56	8
1990	102	26	76	43	54	5
1991/92	79	23	56	29	41	9
Average 1987 to 1991/92	110	26	84	47	56	7
1992/93	98	30	68	45	50	3

(Averages are rounded to the nearest whole number)

off the A12 road on to the main line and was run into by the driving van trailer of a Liverpool Street to Norwich push-pull express, travelling at 40 mile/h, with the locomotive at the rear. There were no injuries to passengers or traincrew, and the two occupants of the car managed to scramble clear before the collision.

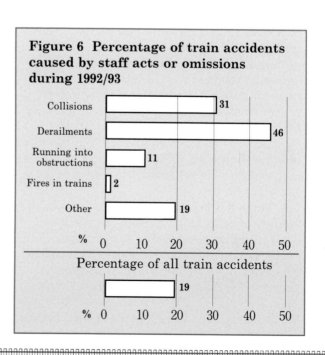

Figure 6 Percentage of train accidents caused by staff acts or omissions during 1992/93

	%
Collisions	31
Derailments	46
Running into obstructions	11
Fires in trains	2
Other	19

Percentage of all train accidents: 19

Accidents at level crossings

103 The number of accidents and reported system failures at each type of level crossing during the year commencing 1 April 1992 is given at Table 6. The accidents included are train and movement accidents, as defined in Chapter 1. The reported system failures are those incidents not giving rise to an accident but which are required to be reported; for example when a train runs onto a protected level crossing when not authorised to do so, or when the crossing equipment fails to operate correctly and provides a reduced level of crossing protection. The casualties arising from the accidents at level crossings are given in Table 7. The casualty figures include all personal injuries sustained in train accidents and both movement and non-movement accidents.

104 The figures for the number of crossings shown in Table 6 are provided by British Railways Board (BRB) and refer only to crossings on BR. The number of crossings on other railways is not shown although reference is made to accidents occurring on these railways and these are shown in the lower part of Table 6. The number of unprotected crossings in some categories varies considerably from those previously recorded. Following the publication of the Requirements for footpath and bridleway level crossings, BR has been undertaking an extensive survey of all footpath and bridleway crossings to determine whether they are in compliance with the Requirements. The numbers of these crossings known has therefore been recalculated as a result of this review. The fluctuations have also resulted from the closure of over 100 private vehicular crossings annually, the provision of telephones at user-worked crossings, or from past errors in recording. The details provided are the latest available. Detailed records of protected crossings are maintained by BRB and the information shown in Table 6 concerning these is therefore more reliable.

105 There has been a reduction by 21% in the number of train and movement accidents at level crossings compared to the previous twelve-month period. There were 55 reported accidents of which 28 involved collisions between a train and a road vehicle.

106 As mentioned in last year's report, because of the potential for a serious train accident and the consequential loss of life, an investigation into road user behaviour at the road traffic light signals at level crossings is to be undertaken for HMRI. The contract for this work has been awarded to the Transport and Road Research Laboratory. Meanwhile BRB has also commissioned consultants to undertake a risk analysis investigation into the operation and use of level crossings. HMRI is co-operating with the railway's consultants in the provision of accident data and BRB has undertaken to make the results of the investigation known to HSE.

Manually-operated gated crossings

107 The number of train accidents at manually-operated gated crossings (MG) has halved since last year with four having occurred. All involved trains running into gates although, once again, it was fortunate that there were neither vehicles nor pedestrians on the crossing when the incidents occurred. In addition, there was a movement accident which resulted in the death of a pedestrian.

108 The four incidents involving gates were as follows:

(a) on *23 June 1992*, on the single line between Tenby and Pembroke, a DMU failed to come to a stand at the Stop board and struck the gates of the train-crew operated *Manorbier Crossing (WR)*, Dyfed. Pieces of the damaged gates struck a tractor which was about to cross the line, fortunately without causing any injuries. The protection of this crossing has since been changed to that of a locally monitored automatic open crossing (AOCL);

(b) having come to a stand clear of *Brampton Fell Crossing (LMR)*, near Carlisle, Cumbria, on *4 November 1992*, the driver of a loaded coal train started to reverse his train onto the crossing without the authority of the signalman. The signalman saw what was about to occur and managed to close the boom gate on one side before the train ran through the other gate;

(c) the wind blew a gate from its catch at *Long Lane* near Northallerton, North Yorkshire, on *27 February 1993*, and it was struck by a passing DMU;

(d) an engineer's train comprising a diesel locomotive and four engineer's wagons

Table 6 Accidents at level crossings

		Protected								Unprotected			
		Manual:			Automatic:					Manual:			
		MG	MCB	MCB with CCTV	AHB	ABCL	AOCR	AOCL	UWC with MWL	UWC	UWC with T	OC	FP
British Railways:	Total												
Number of crossings													
At 31 Mar 92	9231	362	314	283	422	10	5	199	128	4207	918	56	2309
At 31 Mar 93	9091	385	310	299	443	24	3	193	139	3751	990	56	2498
Number of accidents*													
1 Apr 91 - 31 Mar 92	68	8	-	2	13	-	-	9	2	10	14	2	8
1 Apr 92 - 31 Mar 93	47	4	-	-	8	1	-	9	-	6	10	-	9
Number of system failures†													
1 Apr 91 - 31 Mar 92	28	1	7	7	9	-	-	1	2	-	-	1.	-
1 Apr 92 - 31 Mar 93	35	1	3	5	15	4	-	4	2	-	1	-	-
Other railways:													
Number of accidents*													
1 Apr 91 - 31 Mar 92	3	1	-	-	-	-	-	2	-	-	-	-	-
1 Apr 92 - 31 Mar 93	8	1	-	-	-	-	-	4	-	-	-	3	-
Number of system failures†													
1 Apr 91 - 31 Mar 92	-	-	-	-	-	-	-	-	-	-	-	-	-
1 Apr 92 - 31 Mar 93	-	-	-	-	-	-	-	-	-	-	-	-	-

Note: See Appendix 9 for abbreviations used for types of level crossings.

* Train and movement accidents only as defined in Chapter 1.

† Defined as an occasion, not resulting in a train accident, when a train runs onto a protected level crossing when not authorised to do so or when the level crossing equipment fails to operate correctly.

approaching *Penrhyn Crossing*, Gwynedd, on the 1'11½" gauge Ffestiniog Railway was unable to stop due to a combination of the greasy nature of the rails and the sole braking being provided by the locomotive and a brake van. The train slid into the gates at low speed causing minor damage.

109 The accident which killed a pedestrian took place at *Wedgwood Crossing (LMR)*, near Stoke-on-Trent, Staffordshire. Because the crossing is not continuously manned the gates are kept closed at night. Pedestrians can use the crossing by means of non-lockable wicket gates although a warning bell is sounded automatically by approaching trains. However, the crossing was manned on *2 February 1993*, when a woman, who had just alighted from a Down stopping passenger train, used the wicket gate and walked behind the Down train as it was departing. While the warning bell continued to sound, she stepped into the path of an Up express train travelling at 85 mile/h

and was instantly killed. A verdict of accidental death was recorded at the inquest.

Manually-controlled barrier crossings

110 No accidents were recorded at manually-controlled barrier crossings, monitored either directly (MCB) or by means of closed circuit television (CCTV), during the period of this report. There was one report of a train running onto a crossing without authority and two equipment failures on MCB. At CCTV-monitored crossings, incidents of trains running onto crossings without authority were reported on three occasions, two of which were caused by the drivers misjudging the braking at a station, passing a signal at Danger and coming to a stand on the crossing. The third, at *Barnes (SR)*, West London, on *21 May 1992*, was the result of the driver of an EMU passing a signal at Danger that protects both the crossing and a junction. The barriers were raised as the train ran over the road but

Table 7 Casualties in level crossing accidents - all railways

	Total	Protected Manual: MG	MCB	MCB with CCTV	Automatic: AHB	ABCL	AOCR	AOCL	UWC with MWL	Unprotected Manual: UWC	UWC with T	OC	FP
Killed - total													
1 Apr 91 - 31 Mar 92	18	-	-	1	4	-	-	2	1	2	3	-	5
1 Apr 92 - 31 Mar 93	10	1	-	-	5	-	-	-	-	-	-	-	4
Passengers killed													
1 Apr 91 - 31 Mar 92	-	-	-	-	-	-	-	-	-	-	-	-	-
1 Apr 92 - 31 Mar 93	-	-	-	-	-	-	-	-	-	-	-	-	-
Staff killed													
1 Apr 91 - 31 Mar 92	-	-	-	-	-	-	-	-	-	-	-	-	-
1 Apr 92 - 31 Mar 93	-	-	-	-	-	-	-	-	-	-	-	-	-
ORV killed													
1 Apr 91 - 31 Mar 92	7	-	-	-	2	-	-	2	-	-	3	-	-
1 Apr 92 - 31 Mar 93	4	-	-	-	4	-	-	-	-	-	-	-	-
Pedestrians killed													
1 Apr 91 - 31 Mar 92	11	-	-	1	2	-	-	-	1	2	-	-	5
1 Apr 92 - 31 Mar 93	6	1	-	-	1	-	-	-	-	-	-	-	4
Injured - total													
1 Apr 91 - 31 Mar 92	78	-	2	4	54	-	-	12	-	2	1	-	3
1 Apr 92 - 31 Mar 93	42	3	1	4	8	4	-	13	-	5	1	-	3
Passengers injured													
1 Apr 91 - 31 Mar 92	44	-	-	-	43	-	-	1	-	-	-	-	-
1 Apr 92 - 31 Mar 93	6	-	-	-	4	-	-	-	-	2	-	-	-
Staff injured													
1 Apr 91 - 31 Mar 92	8	-	-	1	4	-	-	1	-	1	1	-	-
1 Apr 92 - 31 Mar 93	11	-	1	-	2	-	-	6	-	1	-	-	1
ORV injured													
1 Apr 91 - 31 Mar 92	19	-	1	-	7	-	-	10	-	1	-	-	-
1 Apr 92 - 31 Mar 93	15	-	-	-	2	4	-	6	-	2	1	-	-
Pedestrians injured													
1 Apr 91 - 31 Mar 92	7	-	1	3	-	-	-	-	-	-	-	-	3
1 Apr 92 - 31 Mar 93	10	3	-	4	-	-	-	1	-	-	-	-	2

fortunately there were no vehicles passing at the time. The train was brought to a stand before passing over the junction and thus avoided a collision with a train at the junction. The driver was the subject of internal BR disciplinary procedures. Two equipment failures were also recorded.

111 The only injury reported was on *14 August 1992*, at *Sturry (SR)* near Canterbury, Kent, where a cyclist fell when the wheel of his cycle was allegedly trapped in a gap between the concrete slabs of the crossing deck. The deck was subsequently repaired.

Automatic half-barrier crossings

112 There were three collisions between a road vehicle and a passenger train reported at automatic half-barrier crossings (AHB) all of which were the result of the road vehicle drivers failing to comply with statutory requirements at a level crossing. As a result of these three incidents, four occupants of road vehicles were killed, a further two seriously injured and six passengers and staff slightly injured aboard one of the trains. In addition, there were a further three incidents of trains running into barriers that had been damaged or displaced by road vehicles.

113 Road vehicles longer than 55 feet, or wider than 9ft 6ins, or weighing more than 38 tonnes, are classified as abnormal loads and are generally required to have a police escort. Drivers of such vehicles have a statutory duty to telephone the signalman before attempting to cross an AHB. A duly authorised sign placed at the approach to the crossing explains and reminds the driver of this duty.

114 Following the incident at *Hixon (LMR)*, *Staffordshire*, in *1968*, in which 11 people died, police standing orders have been produced concerning the movement of abnormal loads over AHB crossings. The orders require the police escort to remind the driver that it is his responsibility to telephone the signalman before using an AHB.

115 An abnormal load consisting of a tractor unit hauling a low loader trailer and carrying a large excavator, with a police escort, approached *Mucking Crossing (AR)*, Essex, on *2 April 1992*, and stopped at the sign. The police car went ahead over the crossing to control oncoming traffic while the load was traversing the crossing. The mate of the low-loader driver left the cab and went to the nearer railway telephone situated at the

crossing on the off-side of the road. He was unable to obtain a reply from the signalman and so continued diagonally over the crossing to try the other telephone. This action appears to have been taken by the driver as an indication that he could proceed. However, as the load passed over the crossing the trailer grounded and the vehicle had to be stopped foul of the line. The driver also left the cab and went to the rear of the trailer where means exist to raise and lower the body relative to the wheels.

116 At this point an EMU initiated the road closure sequence but, by then, it was too late to avert the accident. The crossing came into the train driver's view when the train was 180 m away. The braking distance for a train travelling at 60 mile/h is of the order of 720 m. The driver of the train managed to slow the train to about 35 mile/h before the collision occurred. Nevertheless, the leading coach was derailed and badly damaged. Other coaches and signalling, level crossing and overhead line equipment (OLE) were also damaged. It was fortunate that there were no fatal or serious injuries with only the train driver, guard and four passengers suffering minor injuries.

117 The Crown Prosecution Service reviewed the evidence of the incident that had been collected and submitted by the British Transport Police and, after due consideration, decided, in the public interest, against prosecution of either the low-loader driver or his mate.

118 Criminally inclined drivers who attempt to zigzag around the lowered barriers of AHB are a permanent problem. Without recourse to the construction of a length of dual carriageway on each side of the crossing or altering the form of protection, both of which are expensive options, it is difficult to prevent such wanton behaviour. At about midnight on *4 April 1992*, the driver of a motor car containing five young people attempted to zigzag around the lowered barriers at *Thorne Moorends (ER)*, near Doncaster, South Yorkshire, and struck the side of a DMU. The car driver and two sisters were killed and the remaining two passengers were seriously injured.

119 An inspecting officer was appointed as an Assessor to HM Coroner under the Regulation of Railways Act 1871 at the inquest into the deaths; a full report will be published in due course. Evidence was given that the crossing was working normally but that the driver of the car was driving under the influence of

alcohol. The jury returned verdicts that the sisters were unlawfully killed and of misadventure in the case of the driver. In spite of the attendant publicity in national newspapers and all broadcasting services, ten weeks after the fatal incident, a train driver reported a near miss at the same crossing when a car passed the flashing red traffic lights and lowered half-barriers and stopped on the track. The car driver saw the approaching train and reversed clear of the crossing but was not apprehended.

120 On the morning of *28 November 1992,* a 17-year-old girl, having passed her driving test about a week before, drove past the flashing red traffic lights and through the lowered half-barrier of *Star Lane (SR),* near Wokingham, Berkshire, into the side of an EMU; she was instantly killed. It is believed that the rising sun shining in her eyes, coupled with her inexperience, were contributory factors in the accident. HM Coroner's inquest returned a verdict of accidental death. In addition, five incidents were reported by train drivers of near misses with road vehicles which passed over the railway just in front of a train. At *Brasswell (ScR),* near Dumfries, on *5 December 1992,* a motorist became increasingly impatient when the barriers failed to rise when a DMU failed and stopped after it had initiated the operation of the crossing equipment. The motorist simply drove through the barriers which caused over three hours delay to road and rail services.

121 Incidents of trains running into barriers which had been damaged or displaced by road vehicles occurred at *Wharf Road (AR),* Hertfordshire, between Cheshunt and Broxbourne, on *3 July 1992, Cornton (ScR),* near Stirling, Central Region, on *28 January 1993* and *Litlington (ER),* near Royston, Herts, on *15 March 1993.* No injuries were reported in any of these incidents.

122 Last year two pedestrians were accidentally killed on AHB crossings, this year only one fatality was reported. An eighty-year-old man, with a history of being muddled and confused and of wandering from home, was seen lying on the track at *Duxford (AR),* Cambridgeshire, on *11 January 1993,* where he was struck and killed by a freight train. The jury at HM Coroner's inquest returned a verdict of accidental death. In another accident, a 15-year-old cyclist was seen to wait on the right-hand-side of the road for an Up passenger train to pass at *Bramley Station (SR),* Hampshire, on *22 April 1992.* While the barriers remained down, the road traffic lights were showing and

the audible warning sounding. Despite these warnings he started to cross the line and was struck by a Down DMU which was to stop at the station. The youth suffered severe internal injuries together with fractures of the arm and shoulder.

123 In an another incident a man killed himself at *Milford (SR),* Surrey, on *23 January 1993.*

124 There were four failures when trains ran onto level crossings before the barrier lowering sequence had been completed. Signals passed at danger or failure to control the train when stopping at stations were the cause of incidents at *Queen Adelaide (Lynn Road) (ER)* near Ely, Cambridgeshire, on *15 September 1992* and *Sawbridgeworth Station (AR),* Hertfordshire, on *28 September 1992.* At *Sandy Lane (WR),* Oxfordshire, between Banbury and Oxford, on *9 June 1992,* the crossing was on local control and, when the signalman was distracted, he forgot to advise the attendant to lower the barriers as a passenger train approached the crossing. A motor car was fortunate in being able to stop just before the train went across the road. At *Westerfield (AR),* Ipswich, Suffolk, on *30 November 1992,* a DMU passed the station starting signal by less than a metre and initiated the barrier lowering sequence. While the train driver gave up the token for the Woodbridge to Westerfield radio electronic token block section and completed his station duties, the barriers remained down. He was given permission to proceed providing the barriers remained down. However as the train started to move, the approach-locking timing-out period was completed and the barriers started to rise. Before they were completely up, the train re-initiated the lowering sequence, causing the barriers to strike a car which had just started moving over the crossing. The car was able to stop and reverse clear of the crossing.

125 There were 11 occasions when the equipment failed to provide the full protection required for the rail or road user. At *Forteviot (ScR),* near Perth, Tayside, on *9 November 1992,* contractors, who were to excavate a channel under the track for a communications cable, had been refused permission to start work until they had been fully briefed on the safety implications of working close to the railway and a level crossing. They nevertheless started work and jammed a piece of wood into the barrier mechanism preventing it lowering at the approach of a train. Because of the inherent danger to the railway, BR was required to seek and were granted an interim

interdict preventing the contractors carrying out further work within 25 yards of the railway.

126 After extensive testing, it was found that a build up of copper dust had caused an electrical short circuit in the barrier control detection unit that led to the barriers failing to lower at *Pooley Green (SR)*, between Staines and Egham, Surrey, on *3 April 1992*. All similar crossings within the South Western Division of SR were examined to prevent a recurrence.

127 Although a fault was reported at *Folly Bank (ER)*, near Peterborough, Cambridgeshire, on *14 April 1992*, everything was subsequently found to be in working order. A further fault was reported on *25 April 1992*, and the failure was finally traced to a faulty treadle cable.

128 The barriers failed to lower at *Bainton Green (ER)*, also near Peterborough, on *3 May 1992*, where preparatory work was in hand at the crossing in connection with an increase in line speed. Details are given in Chapter 6 under wrong side signalling failures (WSF).

129 Failures of both telephones (treated as WSF) were reported at *Quarrington (ER)*, near Sleaford, Lincolnshire, on *13 July 1992* and *Milton Fen (AR)*, near Cambridge, on *30 January 1993*. The other incidents were reported at *Eastrea (ER)*, Cambridgeshire, on *19 June 1992*, *Smithfield Road (ER)*, near Brigg, Lincolnshire, on *27 August 1992*, *Lucks Road (LMR)*, on *13 April 1992* and at *Hixon (LMR)* near Stafford, on *27 February 1993*.

130 It is of concern to learn that at *Quarrington (ER)*, near Sleaford, on *11 December 1992* and again on *25 January 1993*, two similar incidents occurred at about 20.00 during the hours of darkness. Two motorists mistook the crossing for the entrance to a nearby hospital and turned at the crossing to finish on the track and foul of trains. Fortunately, in neither case was there a train approaching and there were no injuries or further damage. In addition there were 36 incidents of motor vehicles striking level crossing equipment which caused sufficient damage to prevent trains from passing over until the crossing had either been manned or repairs carried out. A further eight instances were reported where the damage by motor vehicles was minor and did not affect the operation of trains.

Automatic barrier crossings locally monitored (ABCL)

131 The first collision between a train and a road vehicle has been reported since this comparatively new type of crossing protection has been adopted by BR. At 13.20 on *2 January 1993*, a car containing two adults and two children was standing at a lowered half-barrier at *Beccles Bypass (AR)*, Suffolk, in extremely foggy weather when a van collided with the rear of the car, pushing it through the barriers and onto the line where it was struck by a DMU. The car was carried approximately 100 m along the line, resulting in the driver being trapped inside and critically injured. The remaining passengers in the vehicle escaped with comparatively minor injuries. The van driver was prosecuted and pleaded guilty. He was fined and had eight penalty points imposed.

Automatic open crossings remotely monitored

132 There were no incidents at the three automatic open crossings remotely monitored (AOCR) that remain in operation.

Automatic open crossings locally monitored

133 Automatic open crossings locally monitored (AOCL) are protected solely by road traffic signals which are initiated automatically by an approaching train. The train driver must see an indicator light showing that the traffic signals are operating before continuing across the road. There were a total of 13 train accidents, the sole cause of which were road vehicle drivers ignoring the traffic signals and colliding with a train. There were no fatalities as a result of the collisions. This compares with eleven collisions in the previous twelve months which resulted in two deaths.

134 The most serious incident in terms of possible consequences occurred on *8 May 1992*, at *Seal Sands*, where a goods line crosses a public road on land owned by the Tees and Hartlepool Port Authority. A road tanker, loaded with diesel oil, collided with a freight train consisting of four discharged hydrocyanic acid tank wagons hauled by a Class 47 locomotive. The road tanker overturned following the collision, trapping the driver in the cab. There was a leakage of diesel oil from the road tanker which was dealt with by the emergency services. The railway wagons were undamaged so there was no leakage of the highly toxic remnants of the load.

Two members of the train crew suffered shock

Collision between a road tanker and a freight train at Seal Sands near Billingham on 8 May 1992.
Photograph courtesy of Northern Echo.

and minor injuries, a third crew member and the tanker driver, although their injuries were not serious, were detained in hospital overnight. The tanker driver was later successfully prosecuted for failing to comply with the road traffic signals.

135 On a private road within the Grangemouth Oil Terminal, at *Tongues*, on *15 April 1992*, a lorry collided with a BR locomotive. The train driver stated that he had seen the indicator light showing that the road traffic lights were functioning. The locomotive's driver and guard together with the lorry driver were treated for shock. Another collision occurred between a motor car and a BR locomotive at the same location, on *23 March 1993*, resulting in minor injuries to the occupant of the road vehicle. Again no fault could be found with the road traffic signals. A similar accident was reported last year when a taxi was in collision with a BR locomotive at the same crossing. Alterations are now being undertaken to provide road users with an improved advance warning of the approach to the crossing and a better view of the traffic light signals.

136 The drivers of motor cars involved in incidents on the same day, *17 June 1992*, received slight injuries when one collided with a freight train at *Seaton (ER)*, Northumberland, and the other with a passenger train at *Umberleigh (WR)*, near Barnstaple, Devon.

The driver of the freight train was also treated for shock. A motorist was also slightly injured when his car collided with a passenger train at *British Cellophane (LMR)*, near Barrow-in-Furness, Cumbria, on *20 June 1992*. The car driver admitted passing the road traffic signals while they were showing.

137 Failure by motorists to comply with the road traffic signals also caused collisions between motor vehicles and trains without resulting in injury. Such incidents occurred at: *Salem Street*, on the railway line of Associated Octel Company Limited, Anglesey, on *18 April 1992*; *Regent Road (LMR)*, near Bootle, Merseyside, on *6 November 1992*; *Plasser (WR)*, West Ealing, on *27 July 1992*; *Dingwall (ScR)*, Highland Region, on *16 October 1992*; *Halkirk (ScR)*, near Georgemas Junction, Highland Region; the junction for Thurso on the Inverness to Wick line, on *11 January 1992*; *Ingate Street (AR)*, near Beccles, Suffolk on *5 December 1992*; and *London Road, Beccles (AR)*, on *13 September 1992*. The protection of the crossing at the last location has since been changed to ABCL under the Stott criteria. In each of these cases, the road traffic lights were checked immediately after the incident and were found to function in accordance with their design.

138 A woman slipped and fell, fracturing her wrist on *11 December 1992*, while walking

across *Hayward (AR)* near Woodbridge, Suffolk. The crossing was examined and the road surface was found to be contaminated with oil.

139 There were four occasions on which a train driver passed an indicator when the flashing white light was not showing and went on to the crossing without first coming to a stand, fortunately while no traffic was passing. Two of these incidents occurred at *Kempston Hardwick (LMR)*, between Bedford and Stewartby, Bedfordshire. The protection of this crossing has since been changed to ABCL under the Stott criteria.

Crossings equipped with miniature warning lights

140 There were no reported accidents on crossings equipped with miniature warning lights (MWL) although near Thirsk, North Yorkshire, HM Coroner recorded a finding of suicide on a pedestrian found on *Parvin's (No 81) (ER)*, on *8 January 1993.*

141 There were two incidents of trains running onto crossings without authority. Approaching *Wareham (SR)*, Dorset, on *8 November 1992,* the driver of an EMU failed to stop at a signal at Danger and ran onto the crossing. The driver realised that he was not able to stop before reaching the crossing due to slippery rails and therefore sounded the warning horn. The signalman at Wareham signalbox saw the train driver's difficulties and changed the MWL indication manually to red as the train reached the crossing.

142 During engineering work in the hours of darkness near *Chilham Mill (SR)*, Kent, on *21 February 1993,* the driver of an engineer's train comprising two locomotives and 15 loaded hopper wagons thought he saw a green hand signal being displayed giving him authority to set back over the crossing. The green light was in fact the MWL indication to level crossing users that the line was clear to cross. A member of the public reported that the train had passed the crossing at very low speed while the green light was showing. The crossing is not equipped with wrong line controls and a change to the BR Rule Book no longer requires the MWL to be extinguished during possessions.

Accidents at unprotected crossings

143 At unprotected crossings, the primary responsibility for safety is that of the user.

There are 56 open crossings (OC) on public roads with little vehicular traffic and low rail speeds where the road traffic is required by standard road traffic signs to give way to rail traffic. There are some 2500 public footpath and bridleway crossings (FP) where the statutory duty of the railway is to provide gates or stiles and convenient approaches. The standard 'Stop, Look Listen, Beware of Trains' signs are displayed. Additionally there are some 4000 private vehicular crossings with gates (UWC) opening away from the railway, operated by the user with a notice explaining how the crossing is to be used. Some of these are equipped with telephones connected to a signalbox (UWC with T).

144 During the year, 28 accidents were recorded on unprotected crossings, compared to 34 last year. Eleven were collisions between road vehicles and trains and three arose from trains running into gates which had swung past their stops into the path of the train. There were a further four incidents of cattle or horses being struck by trains mainly after straying onto the line by way of open gates. The remaining eight were pedestrians or cyclists being struck by trains while using the crossings.

User worked gated crossings

145 User worked gated crossings form the largest category of crossings on BR with about 4000 known crossings. These crossings are restricted to nominated persons and only invitees of the nominee are, in theory, permitted to cross. Their use varies from about 50 vehicular crossings per day to once or twice a year, to almost never. Gates are provided which open away from the railway and users are statutorily obliged to close the gates after use.

146 A motor car was struck by a DMU on the single line between Shrewsbury and Welshpool at *Lame Bridge (WR)*, on *21 July 1992.* The car driver escaped with a fractured collar-bone although his car was a complete write off. The line speed is 70 mile/h and, with the sighting distance of the train from the crossing reported as 210 yards, the minimum time the motorist had to cross the line was just over six seconds. A telephone has since been provided at the crossing.

147 A post office van was in collision with a DMU on *19 March 1993,* on the single line crossing at *Llechryd (LMR)*, near Tal-y-bont, Gwynedd. Both the van driver and train driver

suffered minor injuries and a train passenger sustained a whiplash injury. The sighting distance was 500 yards and, with a line speed of 50 mile/h, the minimum sighting time was 20 seconds which is the standard to which BR are working.

148 The driver of a Hunts Cross to Southport EMU was absent from duty for more than four days suffering from shock after his train struck a car at *Clover-le-Dale (LMR)*, between Freshfield and Ainsdale, Merseyside, on *3 October 1992*. The car driver escaped injury.

User worked gates with telephones

149 Where sighting distances are insufficient at user worked gates, and it can be justified by the number or nature of the users, BR may provide a telephone to enable the user to seek the advice of the signalman before crossing the line. While these are a useful addition to safety, particularly on lines that are fully track-circuited or where signal-boxes are a relatively short distance apart, they are not a universal panacea since signalmen are not always aware of the location of trains in relation to the crossing and there is an apparent reluctance on behalf of level crossing users to use the telephone or wait for a train to pass if told to do so.

150 During the year there were six incidents of motor vehicles colliding with trains at crossings with user worked gates provided with telephones. In each case it was established that prior to crossing the motorists had failed to telephone the signalman in accordance with notices posted at the crossing. The accidents all happened during daylight.

151 On *16 June 1992*, the gates of *Bruichnain (ScR)*, near Inverness, had been left open by a previous user. A motor-cyclist, who was a local resident and conversant with the operation of the crossing, seeing the open gates, attempted to drive across without either stopping or using the telephone; he collided with the rear portion of a two-car DMU travelling at 65 mile/h. The train driver was unaware that the collision had occurred until he was advised by the signalman. The mother of the motor cyclist was following her son in a motor car and was able to summon the emergency services. The motor-cyclist sustained severe injuries including the amputation of a finger, several fractures and multiple lacerations.

152 No injuries were reported in the remaining collisions between road vehicles and trains at UWCT. Collisions occurred between a motor car or light van and a passenger train at *Shadwell (AR)*, near Thetford, Norfolk, on *11 August 1992, Club Lane (LMR)*, between Ormskirk and Preston, Lancashire, on *29 August 1992* and *Colledge West Lodge (ER)*, near Haltwhistle, Northumberland, on *3 October 1992*. A motor car collided with a freight train at *Blackhorse Drove (ER)*, near Littleport, Cambridgeshire, on *6 June 1992* and a lorry collided with a locomotive at *Hollands (SR)*, Sittingbourne, Kent, on *8 August 1992*.

153 The other category of train accident that gives concern at UWCT is collisions with cattle. Because of the time involved in herding cattle across the line, telephones are recommended. At *O'Neill's (AR)*, Elmesthorpe, Leicestershire, on *19 May 1992*, the farmer had sought and obtained permission from the signalman to drive a herd of cattle across the line. However, the signalman did not prevent the approach of a DMU which resulted in three beasts being struck by the train and killed. The signalman has been the subject of the BR internal discipline procedures. BR has accepted liability and met claims for damages.

154 A gate left open at *Ynys (LMR)*, near Machynlleth, Powys, on *22 February 1993*, resulted in a herd of cows straying onto the line where they were struck by a DMU. Four cows were killed and the driver of the train suffered from shock. As a freight train approached *Castleton (SR)*, near Sherborne, Dorset, on *11 June 1992*, the driver of the locomotive saw a herd of cows standing on the line apparently waiting for a gate to be opened. The train struck the herd, killing ten cows and injuring another. When questioned, the farmer was insistent that the gates had been properly closed after he had previously crossed the line and it was concluded that one of the cows, while standing in the waiting bay, had managed to open a gate with its tongue. The gate would swing open when it was unlatched. A chain and padlock has been provided by BR and the farmer has undertaken to secure the gate in future.

Open crossings

155 Open crossings (OC) do not have gates or traffic lights; road signs instruct motorists to give way to approaching trains. The trains are restricted to travelling at very slow speeds approaching and passing over the road. All three accidents in this category were collisions on open crossings on railways not within the control of BR.

156 On *8 and 22 May 1992*, BR freight locomotives struck a car and a lorry respectively on crossings within the docks of Associated British Ports. The first occurred at *King George Dock, Hull*, Humberside, and the second at *Compass Road, Cardiff*, South Glamorgan. Neither the locomotives nor the vehicles were severely damaged although the driver of the lorry did sustain minor head injuries.

Footpath crossings

157 Five pedestrians were reported as being struck by trains and killed on footpath crossings (FP) during the year. Of the three inquests already completed, a verdict of suicide was recorded in one instance and an open verdict in another while the third was considered to have been an accident.

158 The driver of a passenger train travelling at about 45 mile/h alleged that he saw an elderly lady walking very slowly across *Wreake College Foot Crossing (LMR)*, between Leicester and Melton Mowbray, on *29 July 1992*. Prolonged sounding of the train's horn had no apparent affect and, as the train approached, she fell down on the line and was killed by the train. It has not yet been determined whether the fall was accidental or deliberate.

159 A 60-year-old man was struck and killed by an express parcels train at night on *9 December 1992* at *Thristlington (ER)*, County Durham. An open verdict was returned. Following a similar incident during the hours of darkness on *18 February 1993*, the body of a middle-aged woman was found at *Globe Foot Crossing (WR)*, near Stroud, Gloucestershire. The verdict of HM Coroner's inquest was that she had been accidentally killed.

160 At 06:19 on *19 March 1992*, an 80-year-old man was seen to start across *Catneys Foot Crossing (SR)*, Kemsing, Kent. When the train sounded its warning horn he turned around and apparently attempted to move clear of the track. He, too, was struck and killed; the inquest was still awaited at the time of writing.

161 One other person took his own life by standing on *Penney's Crossing (ER)*, between Retford and Doncaster, at 04.30 on *28 May 1992*, until he was struck by a freight train.

162 A woman was standing, leaning too close to the line at *School Crossing (WR)*, between Kidwelly and Ferryside, Dyfed, on *22 August 1992*, trying to attract her dog across the line. Despite a warning horn being sounded by an approaching DMU, both the woman and the dog were struck. The woman's arm was severed in the incident.

163 In another incident, as an EMU approached *Pegamoid Crossing (ER)*, between Ponders End and Angel Road, North London, during the evening of *9 October 1992*, the driver of an EMU travelling at 85 mile/h saw through the darkness a cyclist on the crossing. The driver made an emergency brake application but could not avoid the cyclist. A night watchman at a local factory witnessed the incident and stated that the cyclist had sustained a small cut on the hand. He had left the site immediately and could not be found or identified. The watchman said that the cyclist appeared to be under the influence of alcohol before the incident. The bicycle was found trapped beneath the train; it was removed so that the train was able to continue its journey. The train driver, fearing that he had run over the cyclist, was unable to work for more than three days, suffering from shock.

Classification

164 Although some minor locomotive fires, not amounting to train accidents, are treated as failures, as are station and lineside fires, they are included here rather than in Chapter 6 on Failures. The statistics are included in Appendices 3 and 4 with details of fires on LUL in Chapter 8.

Station and lineside fires

165 During the last year, there has been a 30% increase in station and lineside fires on BR.

166 Several fires occurred on the deck timbers of underbridges on electrified lines of the direct current, contact-rail system, one of the disadvantages of which is that arcing, between the live rail and the contact shoe, often ignites combustible material at ground level. Where such tinder is impregnated with grease, what might otherwise have been a short-lived flare of flame can quickly become a serious fire. Several small fires on *Kew Bridge (SR)*, Greater London, between Kew Gardens and Gunnersbury, carrying the Richmond to Willesden Junction Line over the River Thames, were extinguished in little more than an hour from a London Fire Brigade fire boat on *21 June 1992*. The crew of the 07:10 Edinburgh to Bournemouth passenger train, on *25 July 1992*, were cautioned regarding a fire on the bridge carrying the main line over the River Avon at *Christchurch (SR)*, Dorset. They

extinguished the fire, caused by arcing, using on-board appliances. Railway staff tried to extinguish the underbridge fire over Vernon Road, *Portsmouth Harbour (SR)*, Hampshire, on *4 March 1993,* using portable appliances, but were unsuccessful and the fire brigade were called out.

167 Arson attacks are another major cause of damage to the railway. Eighteen condemned coaches were destroyed by fire in an arson attack at *Cardiff Canton (WR)*, South Glamorgan, on *15 June 1992,* with further difficulty caused by some of the vehicles still containing blue asbestos. Buildings and other static installations are also frequent targets of arsonists. They usually occur at unmanned installations, for example, a permanent way department shed at *Three Bridges (SR)*, West Sussex, on *11 June 1992*; a relay room at *Kentish Town (LMR)*, Greater London, on *28 June 1992*; a waiting room at *Ainsdale Station (LMR)*, Merseyside, on *18 May 1992*; traction power cables at *Fratton (SR)*, Hampshire, on *12 Oct 1992*; signalling and telecommunication cables near *Stratford (AR)*, Greater London, on *25 June 1992*; a permanent way department complex at *Pendleton (LMR)*, Greater Manchester, on *9 May 1992;* and a newspaper kiosk at *Streatham Common Station (SR)*, Greater London, on *2 May 1992*. The destruction of the relay room at Kentish Town led to the loss of signal interlocking between St Pancras, Farringdon and Kentish Town. It took over two months to replace.

Table 8 Reported station and lineside fires 1992/93

Type of location	BR	LUL & DLR	Other Rlys	Total
Lineside, bridges, etc	81	11	-	92
Stations on surface	18	1	-	19
Signal-boxes, sub-stations, etc	7	-	-	7
Other surface locations and neighbouring property	5	-	-	5
Running tunnels	1	10	-	11
Underground station platforms	-	-	-	-
Underground passages, booking halls including tenants' shops, etc	-	8	-	8
Escalators, passenger lifts, etc	-	6	1	7
Underground signal-boxes, sub-stations, switchrooms, etc	-	-	-	-
Underground station offices, booking offices, staff rooms, service tunnels, etc	-	1	-	1
Total	**112**	**37**	**1**	**150**

168 Of the 150 station and lineside fires reported, the following were causes for 50.

Arcing	18
Arson	14
Technical	13
Staff/contractors	3
Controlled fires	2
Total	50

Fires on trains

169 During the year there were 202 reported incidents of fires on trains which were subsequently classified as accidents; 178 occurred on passenger trains and 24 related to freight trains. The majority of the classified accidents required fire brigade attendance.

170 A comparison with the totals for preceding years is shown in Table 9.

Table 9   Number of train fires 1986-1993

Year	Passenger train fires	Freight train fires	Total fires
1987	139	52	191
1988	170	59	229
1989	199	84	283
1990	205	52	257
1991/92	192	33	225
Five year average	181	56	237
1992/93	178	24	202

171 The total number of train fires for 1992/93 was 10% less than in 1991/92.

172 With regard to passenger train fires, an increase in the number of malicious attacks has been accompanied by a reduction in the overall number of fires arising out of technical defects.

173 The number of reported freight train fires showed a significant reduction of 27% when compared with the previous year's figure.

Fires started by passengers

174 Of the 69 passenger train fires caused by passengers, only six were probably due to carelessness, the remaining 63 were due to vandalism. The number of malicious attacks shows an upward trend, increasing by more than 50% above those recorded for the previous two years.

Empty coaching stock

175 A total of three fire incidents were reported in this category, two occurred on DMUs and one on an EMU.

Fires on diesel locomotives

176 A total of 56 fire incidents were reported on diesel locomotives, 25 of which were classified as 'accidents' with the remainder so minor they were classified as technical failures.

177 On *26 March 1993* it was reported that sparks were coming from the leading diesel locomotive of five locomotives coupled together en route from Bescot to Willesden. The train driver stopped his train and reported to the signal box that one of the locomotives had dragging brakes. The locomotive brakes were released and the train was allowed forward at a restricted maximum speed of 50 mile/h. Thirty minutes later the train driver advised that the leading locomotive was on fire at *Stonebridge Park (LMR)*. The fire brigade were summoned and, to allow the use of fire hoses, all lines were blocked for half-an-hour.

Fires on diesel mechanical multiple units

178 The total number of fires on diesel mechanical multiple units (DMU) was 47, only seven of which were started maliciously, the remainder being attributable to technical causes.

179 A DMU en route from Milford Haven to Portsmouth Harbour came to a stand near *Fareham*, Hampshire, on *19 February 1993*, with a fire in the engine of one of its coaches. The traction supply was switched off, while the fire was extinguished by the train crew using automatic and manual fire extinguishers. Subsequent examination of the coach revealed that the fire had been caused by a defective starter motor which had burnt out.

180 On Monday *27 July 1992*, a driver and guard were awaiting their next journey from *Rose Hill Station*, Marple, to Manchester Piccadilly, when the driver noticed smoke appearing from the side of the DMU. After shutting down the engines as a precautionary

measure, the driver and guard alerted station staff and made strong attempts to extinguish the fire. The whole of the underside of the unit was ablaze, denying access to shut off the fuel. The fire brigade, summoned by station staff, quickly controlled the fire enabling access to the fuel control valve which was then turned off. Following investigations, the evidence showed that the fire had started on the track area, the most likely cause being a discarded match or cigarette stub thrown onto the track where the fire was fuelled by a quantity of rubbish and oil-soaked ballast, which ignited easily. The fire quickly spread to the unit assisted by oil impregnated dirt on its underside. In order to avoid a recurrence, additional stone has been placed on the four-foot area and arrangements made to remove it regularly.

Fires in High Speed Trains and diesel-electric multiple units

181 There were nine fires reported on HSTs. This figure is in accord with the numbers reported in previous years and is consistent with the total train miles run by these units.

182 Relatively few DEMU vehicles remain in service and there were no reported train fires in this category.

Fires in electric locomotives

183 No fires were reported in this accident classification, this compares with three fires last year and one fire in the previous year.

Fires in electric multiple units

184 During the year a total of 100 fires were reported on EMUs of which 13 were on LUL passenger trains. Out of these 100, two were ascribed to passenger carelessness, 48 were caused by malicious attacks, five by defective brakes and the remainder were attributed to other technical defects.

185 On *26 April 1992*, the driver of an EMU travelling from Southend Central to *Ockenden (AR)*, Essex, observed that the pantograph of the rear unit was on fire. The pantographs were lowered and the train taken out of service. Later examination revealed a broken pantograph bracket, consistent with having struck an object on the overhead line equipment.

186 The driver of a Crewe to Leeds train reported, on *11 June 1992*, that a Manchester to Leeds EMU had passed him with its rear vehicle on fire. The driver of the affected train confirmed the fire, an emergency isolation of the OLE was taken and the emergency services were summoned. After the fire was out, further investigation revealed the cause to be the bursting of a traction motor armature. The unit, which was scheduled for removal from service in November 1992, was withdrawn immediately.

Fires in passenger coaches

187 In locomotive-hauled coaches and HST coach formations there were 13 reported fires; eight were the result of vandalism, one of public carelessness through a discarded cigarette end and the remaining incidents were due to technical defects.

188 While travelling on a loco-hauled passenger train from Waterloo to Exeter St Davids, on *17 November 1992*, an off-duty member of British Rail staff operated the emergency communication apparatus after hearing a loud bang underneath the train and seeing smoke in the coach. On examination of the train, the train crew found a defective alternator the drive belts of which were smoking. Passengers were removed from the affected coach and the train continued at 5 mile/h to *Woking (SR)* where it was terminated. The cause of the incident was attributed to an alternator/stabilising rod breaking off. This resulted in loss of tension on the pulley belts which were free to rotate around the drive wheel causing friction and smoking. Following reports that the communication cord had not operated correctly, a full test revealed stiffness in operation, the linkages and valves were lubricated and on retesting the apparatus was found to work correctly.

189 When travelling between Liverpool Street and Walton-on-Naze, on *18 January 1993,* an electric locomotive-hauled train with nine coaches was stopped at *Harold Wood (AR)*, Greater London, after it was reported that one of its coaches was filling with smoke. The fire was dealt with by an off duty fireman and a guard using a fire extinguisher. The train service was terminated and passengers continued their journey on a relief train. The fire brigade attended and gave clearance for the train to be moved. A severe electrical flashover on a motor alternator was the cause of the fire.

190 On *12 February 1993*, the signalman in Preston Signalbox noticed from his display panel that a Glasgow to Birmingham train appeared to be at a stand near *Euxton Junction (LMR)*. He contacted staff at Leyland Station who confirmed that the train was indeed stationary with smoke coming from the rear coach. Until the arrival of the fire brigade the train crew and a train driver travelling as a passenger on the train, fought the fire. The OLE was isolated and all lines were blocked to traffic. After the fire brigade had brought the fire under control a shunting locomotive was despatched to remove the damaged vehicle.

191 There were no injuries to passengers. A number of mail bags were destroyed and the interior of the coach was completely burnt out. Extensive investigations revealed the cause of the fire to be a faulty electrical heater igniting combustible materials such as passengers' luggage and mail bags piled in close proximity to the heater.

Fires in non-passenger vehicles

192 Apart from two on-track machinery fires, and two fires associated with dangerous goods wagons, only one freight train wagon fire was reported throughout the year.

193 Staff at Moss Gatebox, near Doncaster, South Yorkshire, reported smoke coming from beneath an oil tank train travelling from Lindsey to Leeds, on *18 May 1992*. This was later confirmed to be flames by staff at Balne Gatebox. The train, which was conveying motor spirit, came to a stand at *Temple Hirst (ER)*, North Yorkshire, and the emergency services were advised. Flames on the second and eleventh vehicles were extinguished by the fire brigade. The incident was caused by binding brakes igniting fuel spillage.

194 On *27 April 1992*, the fire brigade were summoned to a fire on a battery-powered engineer's train on the *Waterloo and City (SR)* line. After the fire was extinguished the train service had to be suspended for the remainder of the day as a result of smoke in the tunnels. The incident was caused by stray traction return current passing through the engineering train wheels and frame and via the earth cable of the battery charger supply. This fault current exceeded the current carrying capacity of the cable resulting in a breakdown of insulation and subsequent fire. The fault current was not detected by the supply fuse. Improvements to the poor traction return path

will occur when four rail operation is introduced.

Table 10   Number of train fires 1992/93

Type of vehicle	Passenger train	Freight train
Diesel locomotive	6	19
DMU	47	-
HST or DEMU	9	-
Electric locomotive	-	-
EMU	100	-
Passenger coaches	13	-
Empty coaching stock	3	-
Non-passenger vehicles	-	5
Total	178	24

General

195 There are 86 different types of occurrence which are regarded as failures by HM Railway Inspectorate. Examples range from blockage of the line by natural and other causes, to the many failures that can befall structures, track and trains. The majority of cases are unremarkable, doing little more than delay traffic and only a few might achieve notoriety by, for instance, closing a line for an extended period of time. The statistics are given in the lower half of Appendix 3.

196 In the year under review, the total number of failures has increased by 253 over 1991/92, a rise of 16%. One of the largest parts of this increase was blockage of the running line by flood, landslide and other natural phenomena and also by motorists (at places other than level crossings) and contractors.

197 There were 208 cases of flooding of the permanent way and slips in cuttings, etc in 1992/93, compared with only 119 reported in 1991/92. The annual average for the five years 1985-89 was 56, after which the figure rose dramatically in 1990 to 148. There is no evidence that flooding is on the increase, and this discrepancy would appear to result from more assiduous reporting, probably arising from the greater attention given to the subject following the publication of the report into the collapse of a bridge at *Glanrhyd (WR)*, on *19 October 1987*(HMSO 1990 ISBN 0 11 550961 5).

198 Although wanton acts of vandalism are of great concern to the railways, there are instances of railway staff themselves, or contractors, obstructing the line. Postal workers, handling mail at stations, use platform tractors, normally skilfully, towing BRUTE (British Railways Universal Trolley Equipment) trolleys. However, on the night of *18 September 1992,* at *London King's Cross (ER)*, the usual skills were not in evidence. With only five BRUTEs on the drawbar, a postal tractor driver lost control and the fifth fell onto the track. At the same time, the third and fourth trolleys struck the side of a train that was standing at the platform, and broke the driver's window.

Locomotives and rolling stock

199 For the 12 months up to 31 March 1993, the total figure for locomotive and rolling stock failure increased by 6.8% to 375. There has been an improvement in London Underground EMU reliability.

200 The most alarming failure of the year took place on *25 January 1993* and involved the HST power car at the head of a London St Pancras to Nottingham express passenger train, on *25 January 1993*. The driver thought that he had struck something about 200 yards south of Radlett Junction and the train came to a stand at *Napsbury, (LMR)*, Hertfordshire, some $2\frac{1}{2}$ miles further on. Examination revealed certain damage below frame level and also that some 12 inches of flange had broken off No 8 wheel.

201 Immediate investigation, involving a principal inspecting officer, focussed attention on a manufacturing fault in a relatively small batch of wheels, the whereabouts of which were known within hours and urgent examination was conducted within days. No further problem was found.

202 Most failures are less remarkable than that at Radlett. An example was the failure of the locomotive hauling a Cardiff to London Paddington express passenger train in the *Severn Tunnel (WR)*, on *14 April 1992*. Just after entering the tunnel, the hand-brake gear box cover fell from the locomotive and fractured the brake pipe of one of the coaches, disabling the train. An assisting locomotive was brought up from Newport, and the train was able to proceed, ninety minutes later. Delays and diversions were imposed on other trains during this time.

203 The figures for failure of coupling apparatus were artificially reduced for the year 1991/92 due to the omission of a set of reports. These figures have now been corrected in Appendix 3 where they can be compared with 1992/93.

Vehicles carrying dangerous goods

204 Fifteen trains conveying dangerous goods were stopped with reported defects to wagons during 1992/93. Thirteen of the reports concerned tank wagons, ten of which were leaking. There were four reports of binding brakes and one of a defective buffer.

Overhead line equipment

205 There has been a further reduction from 39 to 30 in the number of reported failures of OLE. Weather is often to blame as can be seen from two of the following examples.

206 At *Cornbrook Junction (LMR)*, Greater Manchester, on *13 June 1992*, an electric multiple unit (EMU) suffered pantograph damage while working into Deansgate Station. Subsequent investigation revealed that the pantograph of another EMU had been damaged at the same location some three hours earlier but an isolation had not been considered necessary. It was then felt that some slack had developed in the contact wire due to a very high ambient temperature and a local speed restriction of 10 mile/h would suffice until it became cooler. In the second incident, however, the pantograph had become entangled in the OLE and a registration arm was hanging down, foul of the running lines. The cause of the incident was confirmed as being a slack contact wire owing to exceptionally hot weather.

207 On *23 January 1993*, an EMU working a Helensburgh to Drumgelloch stopping passenger train, suffered severe damage to its pantograph assembly, between *Helensburgh and Dumbarton (ScR)*, from striking OLE which had been displaced by severe gale-force winds. The driver was able to coast to the next station, Cardross, Strathclyde, where arrangements were made to convey passengers forward to Dumbarton over the unaffected Down line. Two days later the force of the wind had abated sufficiently for repairs to be effected.

208 At *Christon Road* Crossover, *Tyne and Wear Metro* (T&W), on *5 August 1992*, pantograph bounce caused damage to the OLE on both the 'In' and 'Out' lines and suspension of services for over six hours, until repairs could be completed.

Wrong side signalling failures

209 The classifications of wrong side failures (WSF) and the numbers reported in each category are shown in Table 11. The total for 1992/93 of 765 is a slight increase over the total for the previous year of 702. The policy of changing lamps in position light signals at regular intervals has resulted in a reduction in the number of filament failures from 189 to 151. However, this improvement was off-set by an

increase of failures attributed to vandalism which led to 124 signals showing no light compared with 59 in the previous year.

210 There was a slight increase in WSF of track circuits (TC) from 267 to 285 largely caused by rail surface contamination by rust or leaves fallen from trees. The increase can probably be accounted for either by reduced traffic resulting in increased corrosion of the rail surfaces or, with those caused by fallen leaves, may indicate improved vigilance by signalmen and a better understanding of the areas where the problem is most acute. One interesting development is that of the track circuit actuator interference detector (TCAID) which can be installed during the leaf-fall periods. It is a battery operated device which will shunt the track circuit when it detects the frequency emitted by a TC shunt assistor fitted to a vehicle. While the equipment is not of a fail-safe design it has operated reliably during the year under report.

211 Improved standards clearly had an effect on the reduction from 12 to zero in the number of failures of TC in the design, test, installation and maintenance deficiency category.

212 The application of improved standards of design and testing is beginning to have an apparent effect in reducing WSF in equipment, other than TC. Incidents resulting from deficiencies in the design, installation, testing and maintenance of equipment have fallen from 61 to 45. Although no train accidents were caused by WSF, as a train approached *Bainton Green AHB (ER)*, near Peterborough, Cambridge, the driver noticed that the barriers were still raised but managed to stop before reaching the crossing. While he was reporting the fault on the telephone the barriers lowered. A circuit intended to make a relay slow to release had been incorrectly wired and under certain circumstances the relay remained energised and the barriers failed to fall. The work had only just been completed and testing had been inadequate. The testing procedures have been reviewed as a result.

213 Late at night the driver of a Dover to Brent freight train saw a proceed aspect at a signal at *Willesden (LMR)*, London, with an indication that his route was over a set of points in the reverse position. However, the points were actually in the normal position and the train was diverted, although fortunately there was no conflicting movement. It transpired that following testing work, test rig

wiring had been left in place while testing continued on other parts of the interlocking. Although the points had been signed into use, a switch on the test rig had been operated to simulate reverse detection of the points even though they were lying normal. As a result, the interlocking identified them incorrectly as lying reverse and set the route. The testing handbook is being analysed to determine whether the deficiency is with the instructions or with staff training.

214 The number of unprotected failures of colour-light signals rose from 21 to 34 in 1992/93 and it is difficult to determine the cause as the signalling concerned covers a few relatively small areas, most of which are being resignalled or are due for resignalling. Current proposals by BR are that only two areas in North Kent will remain in 18 months time.

215 A system of remedial action projects, or RAP, has been introduced by BR by which a project manager is appointed and tasked with improving the reliability of specified pieces of equipment with a view to reducing and ultimately eliminating the numbers of WSF. Among the projects so far initiated are a number concerned with signal lamps, lampholders and filament changeover relays. Others deal with TC failures due to rust or leaf contamination and failures of level crossing telephones.

216 The single incident on LUL was the result of a design error which led to a WSF at *Queen's Park (LUL)*. A driver observed the train stop of the starting signal at which his train was standing lower when a train passed on a conflicting route, although the signal remained at red. Controls are provided to lower the train stop when a reverse direction movement is taking place to prevent 'back-tripping'. A contact of a non-fail-safe route lever had been used to provide this control instead of a signal lever. The route lever had not been replaced after a train movement failed to draw clear and the train stop was lowered while another train was passing.

217 On *Metrolink* an ATP beacon failed to apply the brakes when a vehicle was driven past a signal at Danger under controlled conditions. A junction box was found to have conducting metal residues, formed by the ingress of water which had caused a short circuit. The affected junction boxes have now been changed.

218 On *T&W* a set of points moved when a bogie of a Metrocar was standing on a locking TC which should have prevented the movement of the points. The cause was traced to the failure through fatigue of the copper shunts on all four wheels of the bogie. The shunts between tyre and wheelcentre pass through the resilient insulating rubber blocks to provide electrical continuity from tyre to tyre through the axle to operate TC. One group of rubber blocks appear to be involved and affected tyres are being changed while checks on others continue.

Table 11 Wrong side failures of signalling equipment 1992/93

Cause of track circuit (TC) failures:

(a) rust or rail surface contamination	173
(b) leaf fall contamination	92
(c) bonding deficiencies or insulation failures	15
(d) relay defects	3
(e) cable faults	2
(f) design, test, installation or maintenance deficiencies	0
Total TC failures	**285**
Other equipment design, installation, maintenance or testing failures	**45***

Position light signal failures:

(a) no lights and not light proved	310
(b) all 3 lamps lit at once	1
(c) signals knocked over	13
Total position light signal failures	**324**
Colour light signals - no aspect displayed and unprotected	**34**
Automatic level crossing emergency telephone failure	**77**
Total all wrong side failures	**765**

* Includes 1 on LUL, 1 on T&W and 1 on Metrolink.

Formation and structural failures

219 The importance of routine inspection of structures is illustrated by the two following accounts.

220 At 17:10 on *Friday 27 November 1992*, as a result of routine examination, the central pillar of underline bridge No 99, at *Crane Street Junction (LMR)*, Wolverhampton, West Midlands, was found to be in very poor condition and an emergency speed restriction of 10 mile/h was imposed. The bridge was reported to be due for renewal within months of the examination.

221 Earth tremors recorded around the time may have contributed to the accelerated development of serious fractures in three of the 25 spans of the brick and stone *Frodsham Viaduct (LMR)*, between Chester and Warrington, Cheshire, found during routine inspection on *18 September 1992*. A temporary speed restriction was imposed and repairs were executed over a period of months.

222 On *25 November 1992*, a member of the public informed the West Midlands Fire Service that cracks had appeared in the retaining wall of a railway embankment adjacent to his house in Smethwick, West Midlands, between *Soho North* and *Soho East Junctions(LMR)*. Fire brigade examination revealed that the retaining wall was in danger of collapse but that the embankment seemed to be sound. Later inspection by the civil engineer's staff showed that the track was in poor condition and would need attention. By 01:00 the following morning the wall had been repaired and lifting and packing of the track was started. Less than four hours after reopening the line at 13:30, the electrification engineer reported that one of the OLE structures had moved down the bank and required immediate shoring. It was later decided to erect a new OLE structure.

223 Road vehicles frequently collide with bridges causing structure failure. A reversal of the norm occurred on *15 May 1992*, when a road vehicle was used to enable a failed bridge to be brought back into service. The signalman at *Banavie (ScR)*, Highland Region, could not restore the swingbridge over the Caledonian Canal to carry railway traffic. The civil engineer's staff established that it had disengaged from its drive mechanism and were able to restore it to working order with a gentle nudge from their Land Rover vehicle.

Broken rails

Overall trends

224 Disappointingly, the total number of rail failures reported on the railways of Britain remained virtually the same for the year 1992/93 as for the previous 12 months.

225 British Rail reported a total of 681, four less than in 1991/92, LUL reported 33, the same number as for 1991/92, and Docklands eight, two more than 1991/92. Other railways reported three less, five down to two, so the composition was very little changed from the year before.

226 Of the 33 breakages on LUL 32 were discovered by visual means and only one by ultra-sonic testing. A third of LUL's breakages occurred in switches and crossings (S&C). Rail failures on the Docklands railway remain surprisingly high.

227 The improved sources of information now available to British Rail enables S&C failures to be given as a proportion of the total units in track. The units equate to a turn-out, cross-over, slip, catch-point, or adjustment switch. In the year under review 65 failures in a total of 19 686 units in track gave a failure rate of three per thousand.

228 The failure of 186 welds on BR in a mileage of just under 13 000 miles of continuous welded rail (CWR), represents a failure rate of 14.45 per thousand miles. This compares with a rate of 18.14 in 1991/92, 15.82 for 1990, 20.05 for 1989 and 25.03 for 1988.

229 A study of individual reports suggests a higher rate of weld failures in CWR track which had been installed as serviceable renewals than in track installed with completely new materials. Two-thirds of Train Load Freight's total of 107 breaks at thermit welds occurred in track laid in as serviceable.

230 As indicated in last year's report, the East Coast Main Line, the Leeds Northern Line (Northallerton to Newcastle-upon-Tyne via Teeside and the coast) and the line between Sheffield and Cleethorpes, account for a disproportionately high number of rail failures.

231 The categories under which broken rails are listed in Table 12 cover most of the common types of break. Those listed as 'other' but not associated with rail end or weld

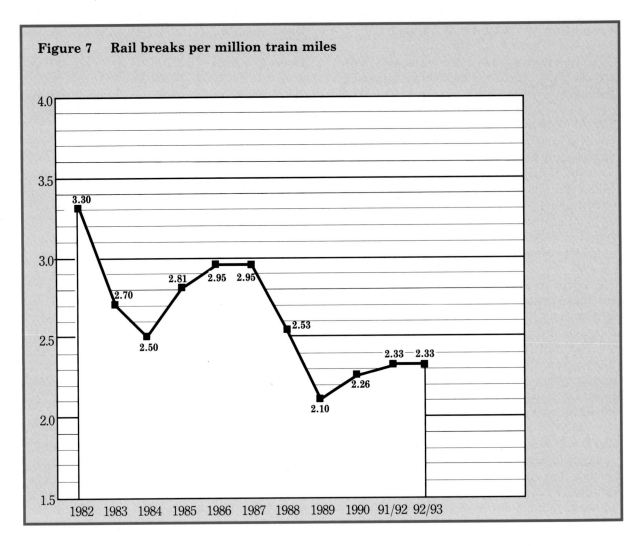

Figure 7   Rail breaks per million train miles

failures have increased on BR over the past few years from 18 (1989), 28 (1990), 41 (1991/92) to 93 in 1992/93. This situation warrants careful monitoring by the operator to identify what types of failure have been included in this category and to establish that they are being properly classified.

232 The rate of breaks per million train miles remains precisely at last year's figure of 2.33. (See Figure 7.) There were no reported derailments as a consequence of broken rails on British Railways.

Track buckles

233 The report which covered the 12-month period April 1991 to March 1992 gave, for the first time, the number of track buckles occurring on the railways in Britain. Not surprisingly all of the buckles reported occurred between April and September so, in effect, they reflected the summer of 1991. Comparison was made with the previous year and noted a reduction from 73 buckles in 1990

to 13 in 1991. Last year, 1992, saw a total of 33 buckles; roughly half occurring in CWR and half occurring in jointed track, and all on British Rail.

234 Of this total 21 occurred in May and 8 in June and, of the 16 which were reported as occurring in jointed track, 13 occurred in May. This points to a lack of preparedness on the part of the railway operator.

235 Temperatures in May and June were above the seasonal average but afterwards the summer weather was poor, giving temperatures lower than the seasonal averages for July and August.

236 There is a widely held belief by traditional permanent way staff that the early summer sees the bulk of track buckles, particularly in jointed track, and the experience of 1992 would appear to reinforce this view.

237 There were no derailments as a consequence of track buckling.

Table 11A Summary of track buckles British Rail 1992

Month	Total	CWR	Jointed
May	21	8	13
June	8	7	1
July	2	1	1
August	1	1	-
September	1	-	1
Total	33	17	16

Damage to bridges by vessels and road vehicles

238 The 'bridge bashing' statistics for British Railways (BR) covering the 12-month period are set out in Table 13. For comparison, the previous years are also tabulated.

239 The figures for underline bridges (bridges carrying the railway) indicate that there has been little change in the overall figures, but an increase in the serious and potentially serious categories. However, the total in these two categories is still less than in 1990.

240 The figures for overline bridges (bridges carrying roads, etc over the railway) indicate that there has been a reduction in the overall figures, but little change in the combined total of the serious and potentially serious categories, although the number of serious incidents trebled. The major problem caused by overline strikes is the deposition of parapet material on the line, but the potential for a complete spandrel wall to be detached or for a main girder to sustain critical structural damage must not be forgotten.

241 HM Railway Inspectorate is aware of a number of incidents affecting bridges on other railways. London Underground are reporting all strikes in the same manner as BR and it is expected that it will be possible to make year-by-year comparisons in the future. In this reporting year, three incidents were reported on London Underground and one on T&W.

242 Good progress was made during the year with the drawing up of amendments to the Road Vehicles (Construction and Use) Regulations, 1986, which will help reduce the likelihood of bridge strikes. It is expected that they will become law towards the end of 1993. There will be three requirements:

(a) for road vehicles with an overall travelling height in excess of 3 m to display a notice in the cab specifying the height;

Table 12 Summary of broken rails showing type of break (figures for 1991/92 shown in brackets)

Type of break	British Rail		LUL & Docklands		Others		All railways	
1 Breaks in plain line								
At rail ends:								
(a) star cracks at bolt holes	132	(112)	8	(8)	-	(-)	140	(120)
(b) other within 600 mm of C/L	63	(56)	6	(8)	-	(-)	69	(64)
At welded joints:								
(a) flash-butt	9	(22)	2	(2)	-	(-)	11	(24)
(b) thermit	177	(208)	-	(-)	1	(-)	178	(208)
(c) other	5	(9)	2	(-)	-	(-)	7	(9)
Away from rail ends and welds:								
(a) transverse (through any part of rail)	125	(166)	8	(6)	1	(5)	134	(177)
(b) surface defects	12	(12)	2	(3)	-	(-)	14	(15)
(c) other	93	(41)			-	(-)	93	(41)
Plain line total	616	(626)	28	(27)	2	(5)	646	(658)
2 Breaks in switches and crossings	54	(48)	13	(12)	-	(-)	67	(60)
3 Breaks in adjustment switches	11	(11)	-	-	-	(-)	11	(11)
Total broken rails	681	(685)	41	(39)	2	(5)	724	(729)

(b) for vehicles with variable height equipment, such as lorries equipped with self-loading cranes, to be fitted with a visual and audible device to warn the driver if at any time while the vehicle is in motion the equipment exceeds the displayed height required in (a) or 3 m, whichever is the higher; and

(c) for all movements on roads by vehicles with a travelling height in excess of 4.88 m to be notified in detail to the appropriate traffic authority and to be agreed by that authority.

This third requirement effectively introduces controls on the movements of very high vehicles and may be considered to be equivalent to the system used in several other European countries of statutory maximum heights with exemptions.

243 The installation of mandatory height restriction signs on non-arch low bridges on trunk roads is almost complete. Fifteen of the twenty high-risk sites also have operational warning systems and three more will be installed soon. The remaining two sites will not have systems installed due to other work eliminating the possibility of a strike. Work is also in progress on warning systems elsewhere.

244 Progress with mandatory signing on local authority roads remains limited. Local authorities have responsibility primarily for road users and select their priorities for mandatory signing on the perceived risk to road users. This may mean that, for example, the priority is given to roads used by double-deck buses. It is debatable whether a railway should make a contribution to costs of re-signing to allow particular bridges to be given a higher priority than would otherwise be the case.

245 Work was carried out during the year on the establishment of design criteria for collision protection beams, and a draft standard has been produced by British Railways. The legal position has now been clarified and beams designed in accordance with the standard are permitted.

246 British Railways, together with the Department of Transport, began a major publicity campaign to highlight the problem. British Railways produced an A5 leaflet (see above) which, as well as giving examples of the problems caused and the costs incurred, encourages drivers to report damage and

Table 13 Damage to bridges by vessels and road vehicles (British Railways)

	Underline bridges			Overline bridges		
	1990	1991/92	1992/93	1990	1991/92	1992/93
Not serious	790	649	647	*125	109	53
Potentially serious	78	50	58		25	15
Serious	11	7	16	4	4	12

* The breakdown of figures for 1990 is not available

bridges whose signing, including warning signing, appears to be inadequate. British Railways have provided a local rate telephone number on which all such reports can be made whichever the railway. The leaflets have been circulated as inserts in trade magazines, but the main thrust has been to enclose a copy with every appointment letter sent to a vehicle operator by the Driver and Vehicle Licensing Agency. During the coming year, every operator in the country will receive the leaflet, as all large vehicles are subject to annual inspections.

Signals passed at danger

247 Because the system for the investigation and classification of incidents where it is alleged that signals have been passed at danger (SPAD) has been slightly altered, the figures published in the annual report have had to be corrected. The final figure for 1991/92 was 944, a reduction of 37 on the figure quoted in the report for that year. That for 1992/93 is 871 although this figure is subject to confirmation. SPAD are not statutorily reportable.

248 Some developments referred to in last year's report are to be tested at selected locations and these include the automatic detonator placer and the special SPAD signal.

249 Two further developments are worthy of note. A draft document has been produced which defines the way in which a hazard ranking can be derived for each SPAD by analysis in a standard consistent way. This provides a priority and indicates possible areas for action either with equipment or with personnel. The other derives from the use of the statistics and details of each SPAD recorded to build up a profile of a driver who may be more likely than others to pass a signal at danger. Interviews are now being conducted with drivers and remedial action, such as additional training, can be provided for those who seem to fit the profile.

250 One of the more hazardous forms of SPAD is starting against a signal. When a train driver has stopped his train at a platform starting signal at Danger there are several stimuli which may cause him to start away but few safeguards. Platform staff or the guard may signal the 'right-away'. For driver-only operation passengers, the timetable and closing the doors may be a distraction and additionally a train may be drawn well up to the signal. The train will have passed over an AWS magnet and the only safeguards are the indication that an AWS warning has been cancelled and the signal itself.

251 Some drivers are in the habit of placing a cap or other object over the power controller or brake as a reminder at a stop signal. This idea has been developed into a button on the instrument panel which when pulled is illuminated red and disables the power controller. To allow power to be taken the button must be pushed in. While this device still depends on driver habit, trials will determine whether it is advantageous and obtain driver reaction.

Major Olver, who retired in October 1992, inspecting a ground frame on the Tanfield Railway, one of his last duties with the Inspectorate.

General

252 The minor railways for which the Inspectorate has responsibility are those lines and locations saved and run by the many railway preservation societies; the museum lines, cliff railways and those run by government departments all, with few exceptions, built under statutory powers and having a gauge of 15 inches or more. The total is in the region of 230; it is difficult to be more precise, as the figures change often.

253 The Inspectorate offers what help it can in the way of advice and encourages prospective operators to join one of the volunteer bodies, such as the Association of Independent Railways (AIR) or the Association of Railway Preservation Societies (ARPS), whose advice will usually be more specific. There was a considerable change in the relationship between the minor railways and the Inspectorate during the year, brought about by the retirement of the Assistant Chief Inspecting

Officer responsible, Major Peter Olver OBE, who had been involved with the preserved lines for 27 years. There can be few people in the country who have anything like his detailed and intimate knowledge of all these railways, many of which have grown, in that time and with his support, into important attractions to their neighbourhood. Liaison with these railways has become the responsibility of the Field Inspectorate, with administrative support and policy advice from London.

254 Another major change that occurred during the year, was the repeal of the Light Railway Act 1896, except as it applies in Scotland, and the introduction of new legislation under the Transport and Works Act 1992, essentially changing the means of obtaining a Light Railway Order (LRO) which is a prerequisite to running a train service. Not least of the changes was the increased cost of the transaction which had itself been a small part of railway preservation. So unpopular was the new measure among the minor railways that the Department of Transport was inundated with applications for LROs prior to the alteration.

Accidents

255 Two clear lessons should be learnt from the accidents and incidents that have happened in the last year. The first is that the operator must beware of unaccompanied children. Railway staff should also be vigilant for unsupervised minors, however briefly their guardians are distracted. Fortunately, no child died falling from a train in 1992/93, although there were four instances of children aged three to ten years falling or jumping from moving trains. The answer to the problem is to ensure that all staff are aware of the danger of small, excited, inquisitive children being hurt in a moment of inattention. The railway has a duty of care to those on its premises and that duty is shared by all members of staff, no matter what else their rostered turn entails.

256 It is disappointing, in a year in which on the whole of British Railways 11 passenger trains were derailed, to find that 12 were derailed on the minor railways. Herein lies the second lesson of the year for, although none of these derailments was of any great magnitude, as they all happened at low speed, 50% were caused by permanent way defects. Railway managers must ensure that an appropriate

New level crossing protection. Flashing yellow lights installed on Volks Electric Railway.

proportion of effort is devoted to track maintenance. It is important to be sufficiently diligent in maintaining the existing infrastructure when involved in other projects requiring a large commitment of similar skills and resources, such as an extension of the line. There will always be abundant volunteers for the more glamorous work such as that on steam locomotives, but an unsound track is an unsound railway and critical attention is bound to be attracted to those lines that have demonstrable shortcomings.

257 Among the other six derailments was one that occurred on the Bure Valley Railway on *26 April 1992*, at *Brampton*, Norfolk, when locomotive *Sian* dropped a spring onto the track, derailing itself. To prevent a recurrence, alterations have been made to the locomotive.

258 On the Llangollen Railway, Clwyd, on *31 August 1992*, the driver and guard of a passenger train both contributed to its derailment. On arrival at *Llangollen Goods Junction*, the driver ran past a stop signal which was set at Danger and then through some trailing points, stopping his train straddling these points. Checking that all was clear in rear of his train, the guard signalled the driver to set back, overlooking the fact that part of his train was on the wrong side of what had become facing points and, damaged or not,

were set wrongly for the intended move. One coach bogie was derailed.

259 There were two collisions during the year, both of a minor nature but both causing injury to passengers, luckily also not serious. The first was while Black Five 4-6-0 No 5025 was running round its train at *Boat of Garten*, on the Strathspey Railway, on *27 May 1992*. While setting back onto the train, the driver failed to control his locomotive adequately and it struck the coaches at about 5-6 mile/h, causing minor injury to five passengers.

260 At *Crewe Heritage Centre*, Cheshire, on *16 August 1992*, a small steam locomotive, hauling two vehicles, collided with a buffer stop at walking pace. A woman passenger, not expecting the train to stop so suddenly, struck her head and received a minor injury.

261 Bristol Industrial Museum runs trains on a short length of the *Bristol Harbour Railway*. On *20 June 1992*, a road 'traffic warden', employed by Bristol City Council, on duty beside the line, stepped or fell backwards into the path of the train and was struck and seriously injured.

262 One of the most alarming events on the narrow gauge was reported to the Inspectorate as a dangerous occurrence under the Reporting

of Injuries, Diseases and Dangerous Occurrences Regulations 1985 (RIDDOR). At *Boston Lodge* works of the Festiniog Railway Company in Gwynedd, on *28 August 1992*, a party of volunteers was engaged in lifting a tender off its wheels and turning it over to leave the frame uppermost. They were using a two-legged, wheeled gantry with two- and four-legged slings, as required, during the lifts. Sleeper packing was used for landing the tender between lifts. At the point of overbalance during the turning movement, the load-bearing sleeper was 'flicked' backwards by the directional change of forces and, as the load was suddenly imposed upon the gantry in an unexpected direction, the gantry moved in reaction until one of its wheels dropped into a flangeway in the workshop floor, effectively 'tripping it up', whereupon it collapsed. Fortunately, the men did not stay to watch events unfold and thus there were no injuries.

263 Most of the injuries to staff and contractors were minor, although some had the potential to be more serious. For instance, a trainee volunteer fireman received minor burns to an arm when he mishandled the oil-firing controls at 'his' end of a Double Fairlie locomotive on the *Festiniog Railway*, Gwynedd, on *28 July 1992*. He was firing the new 0-4-4-0 *David Lloyd George* on its seventh day in service when a 'blow-back' occurred, demonstrating that certain firing controls were insensitive and likely to contribute to this sort of incident. Management decided to change the equipment of their newest locomotive forthwith, standardizing it with the rest of the fleet.

264 A manager on the North Norfolk Railway was examining a locomotive in traffic from the six-foot way in *Sheringham Station*, Norfolk, on *18 October 1992*, when a warning was shouted to him to beware of a shunting movement taking place on the adjacent line. Not hearing properly because of the noise of the locomotive blowing off steam, he stepped away from his position of relative safety and was struck a glancing blow by the shunted stock, causing him to fall and strike his head. The combination of noise, confusion and the lack of someone to look out for him (for he was clearly too engrossed to look out for himself) could have cost him his life. The Railway immediately consulted the Inspectorate and introduced new instructions for staff on or about the track.

'Operation Market'- a 16-stone man is rescued.

LUL systems for managing safety

265 London Underground Limited (LUL) has continued to develop its systems for managing safety. Audits of business units, in many instances for the second time, generally demonstrated their ability to at least maintain if not improve on their original, commendable performance levels. LUL's Company Plan, aimed at reducing staff numbers while similarly maintaining, or improving, levels of safety, started to come into effect and the Inspectorate was kept informed by LUL of these changes. Two major aspects have been a strategic review of staffing for train maintenance activities, and the transfer to respective Line General Managers of track and signal maintenance staff, who were formerly part of central engineering departments.

Revision of LUL's Rule Book

266 Work progressed on LUL with the revision of its Rule Book. Representative groups have considered the tasks that employees undertake and have developed, in many instances, the procedures and processes for the safe execution of these tasks. The first revised rules, now known as procedures, relate to the action to be taken where signals remain at Danger and were issued in February 1993. Procedures covering other topics have since been progressively issued, the final one being scheduled for February 1994.

Emergency exercises

267 In February 1993 representatives of HMRI attended 'Operation Market' featuring a Northern Line train which was, in simulation, stopped and divided by a tunnel collapse. A number of volunteer passengers from the Casualties Union were in various stages of simulated distress ranging from hysteria to heart attack. In preparation for LUL's change of policy later in 1993, a wheelchair-borne passenger was evacuated, initially using the carry-sheet which is now available in trains and at stations. This was not without difficulty since the volunteer carried was 1.93 metres (6 feet 4 inches) tall and weighed 100 kg (16 stones), but the technique proved practicable and many other useful lessons were learned.

Depot security

268 Improved security fencing and CCTV surveillance equipment is being installed at a cost of £11m at 28 train depot sites. There are clearly benefits to LUL associated with the

prevention of graffiti on trains, and in the area of public safety with depots better protected against trespass and the consequent risks from train movements and conductor rails.

Accident record

Train accidents

269 LUL's record of accidents to trains in passenger service remained good with two derailments and a minor incident involving damage to a buffer stop. No injuries occurred in any of these incidents.

270 Both derailments happened on the Northern Line. At *Edgware* the negative shoe of a departing train came into contact with a lead rail on a set of points which resulted in two cars being derailed. The support and safety strap for the negative collector shoe could not be found. With the supporting straps missing the shoe would hang lower than permitted. The second derailment took place at *Mornington Crescent* where the track was unstable at a reconditioning site. The temporary supports were either incorrectly placed and/or inadequate to safely secure the track.

271 Six incidents were reported of trains running into obstructions. In two instances fallen trees blocked the line with the remainder divided between the actions of vandals and railway equipment not clear of the running line.

Movement accidents

272 There were no movement fatalities among staff or contractors, but, unfortunately, 29 passengers or members of the public were killed. This number is generally comparable with the figures of 31 and 33 in the previous two years.

273 Fifteen of the fatalities were confirmed as suicides and verdicts are still awaited on six more. A survey funded by LUL and carried out by a team of researchers from the Charing Cross and Westminster Medical School endeavoured, in broad terms, to analyse the characteristics of the population that attempts suicide on the underground, the factors affecting mortality rates and the psychological problems faced by the train operators involved. The report concluded with a number of recommendations which are or have been addressed. These included the possibility of

platform edge doors and extending the availability of suicide pits, which will be considered by LUL when planning new installations.

274 Most tragic was the passenger movement fatality that occurred at *Hounslow East* one afternoon in January when an elderly lady alighting was seen to be caught by her coat in the doors of a westbound train and to be dragged along the platform, ending up beneath the train. The on-board alarm was operated by passengers who were alerted to her plight by people on the platform and the six-car train stopped with one and a quarter cars remaining in the platform. Hounslow East Station is on the surface and on a curve with inevitably a gap between the platform and the side of the train. LUL has now established a Train Door Safety Group to consider and promote appropriate initiatives and standards.

275 During the year LUL launched a poster campaign. One poster conveyed that obstructing doors can be dangerous, another highlighted the risk of baby buggies being trapped in doors. The Inspectorate also kept train door safety high on its agenda for discussion with LUL and pressed for the best practicable means to be provided and maintained to assist train operators to observe the train side before departing. LUL started a rolling programme of improvements to platform viewing aids where necessary.

276 There was a decrease in the number of notifiable injuries to passengers in movement accidents to 226 from 266 the previous year.

Non-movement accidents

277 There were no non-movement fatal accidents to passengers or staff in 1992/93. The total of passenger injuries was 1271, a small increase on last year's total of 1149. Most of the passenger injuries were associated with stairs and escalators.

278 Non-movement injuries to staff rose to 579, a 16% increase on the previous year. As before, it is sad to report that the greatest single type of staff non-movement accident is being assaulted on duty. Reflecting LUL's concern about this issue, it has created a Staff Assault Working Group which reviews assaults on a regular basis and makes recommendations. It consists of representatives from BT Police, Passenger Services, Safety and Quality Directorate, London Transport Counselling and

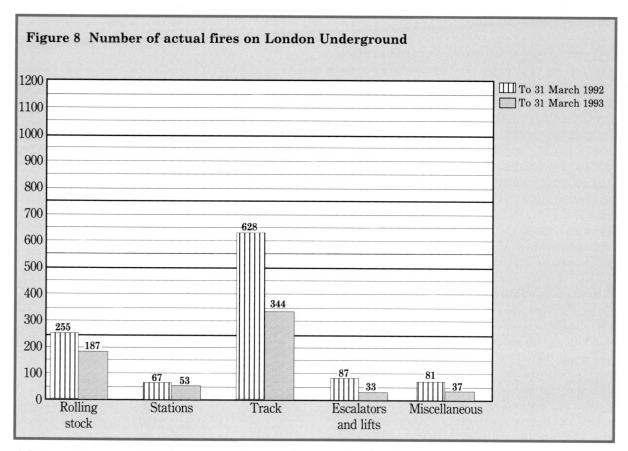

Figure 8 Number of actual fires on London Underground

To 31 March 1992
To 31 March 1993

	Rolling stock	Stations	Track	Escalators and lifts	Miscellaneous
1992	255	67	628	87	81
1993	187	53	344	33	37

Advisory Service and trade unions. Increased training in identifying and defusing potential tensions has featured highly in preventive strategies and personal alarms have been made available to staff.

Fire and smoke incidents

279 The number of fire reports traced to a specific cause or source continued to decrease appreciably as shown in Figure 8 which compares 91/92 with 92/93. Only a small proportion of these fires are statutorily reportable because a condition is that services must be suspended underground for 30 minutes and overground for one hour.

280 The number of fire reports where no cause was found decreased to 2244 compared with 2975 in 1991/92.

New works proposals

Central Line modernisation

281 Inspections of significant phases of the Central Line improvement project were made, including substations, cable works, signalling and rolling stock. Signal equipment rooms between Ruislip Gardens and North Acton were commissioned during the year to a stage enabling both old and new rolling stock to run

on the line. Power supply enhancements were prepared, but the first of the new trains entered service after the period under review.

282 Inspectors kept closely in touch with the progress of this important project and monitored construction, installation and commissioning phases on a sample basis, to ensure that the works were executed safely and are safe for use.

283 The conversion training of 350 train operators (drivers) to the new '92 tube stock in the required time span is being made possible by the use of a £1.2 million cab simulator at LUL's White City Training School. The simulator displays a video film of the complete line including reversing sidings. On the film, signal aspects are changeable, obstructions on the track can be introduced, and the procedure to pass a signal at Danger can be simulated including the approach to a failed train ahead. The simulator also provides training in the new passenger emergency device which features speech communication with the driver. The drivers are given exercises on how to respond to passenger panic situations. The instructors are also able to reproduce foreseeable train faults over a range never before possible, displaying simulated fault data on an information monitor in the cab.

Jubilee Line extension

284 Although actual work has yet to start on the Jubilee Line extension between Green Park and Stratford due to problems with the financial arrangements, development work continued during the year. Given the momentum created by the planning for such a major scheme and the optimism that funding difficulties will be resolved, the project team has progressed work in some instances to tendering stage. HMRI, along with the London Fire and Civil Defence Association (LFCDA), the two main regulatory authorities, regularly meet members of the team to discuss strategic safety issues.

East London line extensions

285 HMRI was also invited to comment in some depth on proposals to extend the East London line both southwards towards Peckham and northwards to Dalston on the North London line of BR. Although both largely utilise old disused railway routes that to the south has been considerably developed so that the re-establishment of a railway is technically, commercially and environmentally more difficult than the northwards extension which would largely run on an existing viaduct paralleling the Kingsland Road.

Angel Station

286 Among a number of station alteration and improvement projects, the most significant was that completed at Angel Station. After a £70 million rebuilding programme, Angel Station, on the Northern Line, was re-opened in September 1992. The notorious island platform, which frequently became congested, has become part of a much wider south-bound platform connected by cross-passages to a new north-bound platform. The increasingly unreliable lifts have been replaced by two sets of three escalators, serving three levels and the station can boast one of the longest sets of escalators in Britain, at 60 metres.

287 Last year's report noted the opening of Manchester Metrolink although the dates of these events fell into the period covered by this year's report. The system was formally opened by HM the Queen on Friday 17 July 1992. What is probably less well known is that on that afternoon, after the royal tram had left for Bury, the final inspection of Metrolink's Piccadilly Station took place and approval was duly given for it to be taken into use; the whole of the initial system then being available for traffic on the following Monday.

288 As the limelight of inspection and formal approval dimmed in Manchester it passed to Docklands Light Railway (DLR) and Sheffield. On the DLR, the planning for the extension beneath the Thames to Greenwich and Lewisham continued while at the same time the work of constructing the extension to Beckton was in full swing. As far as the year under review was concerned preliminary inspections were made of the structures, foundation, embryo stations and, not least, the new depot at Beckton. The decision to replace the GEC signalling with the fundamentally different Alcatel system has meant considerable work in the preliminary proving of that system as it is being applied to DLR. Of equal importance will be the effect next year on the novation of all the individual contracts into one with a single prime contractor, and HMRI was given a series of presentations on how the new arrangements will work in practice. These presentations were generally linked with the regular liaison meetings between DLR and HMRI which have and will continue to be held to discuss new works projects.

289 It was the pattern of these DLR meetings which was followed so successfully in Manchester and has begun in earnest in Sheffield as the hard work of planning has been gradually turned into actual construction. In addition to the series of meetings where general guidance on the requirements to be met on a wide variety of topics can be given, a second series of meetings between the project team, the highway authority and HMRI have been held on the specific subject of the highway alignment and junction layout. As a preliminary to most of the general subject meetings the opportunity has been taken to view the progress of the physical work and to proffer guidance on the likely acceptability of

the work. It must be remembered however that because at this stage the LRT system is still a construction site, the enforcing authority for the HSW etc Act is the local area office of HSE's Field Operations Division. At some point the role of the enforcing authority is transferred to HMRI. This point is determined by mutual agreement but commonly occurs at the time of energisation of the traction power supply systems unless another more suitable opportunity occurs when, say, there is a change of contractor or the operation of trains becomes a significant factor in the work.

290 Contact has been maintained with the promoters of other schemes, the level of activity depending on the stage to which the scheme has advanced. An interesting point arose during the discussions at the parliamentary stage of the proposed system for Leeds. The promoters, West Yorkshire PTE, wished to take the route from one side of the M62 to the other and planned to use part of the clear span where the motorway junction roundabout passed beneath the motorway. The preferred alignment crossed the slip roads at the junction and these were already of sub-standard capacity. The question which had to be resolved, one which would set a precedent, was whether or not the LRT crossing could be safely signalled so as to ensure that there was no blocking back of waiting road traffic onto the motorway itself. A subsidiary question was whether or not adequate sightlines of and for approaching light rail vehicles (LRVs) could be obtained. After considerable discussion a signalled LRV junction was accepted and the fairly severe cost penalty of tunnelling beneath the motorway junction avoided.

291 No serious accidents have occurred this year. However, it was recognised that the reintroduction of large, street-running, rail-borne vehicles would probably lead to a number of road traffic accidents. This was purely a pragmatic view based upon the experience of such systems overseas and of the system in Blackpool. Manchester Metrolink has proved to be no exception to this general rule. Nonetheless a positive approach was taken and, where accidents indicated that some revision to the traffic management arrangements were required, suitable action was recommended and put into effect. There is little that can be done to prevent derailments

caused by poor track, particularly in the highway, other than to relay it. It was, however, driver error which caused the derailment of an Altrincham-bound tram at *Piccadilly Gardens*, Manchester on *12 September 1992*. The tram derailed on the facing points but was travelling slowly and was stopped, with no damage to the tram, within three metres. It was concluded that the driver had failed to notice that the point indicator, which is separate from the signal controlling the movement, was not giving the correct indication. A potentially serious incident occurred at *Hebburn* sub-station *(T & W)* on *16 June 1992* when the 11 kV ac main circuit-breakers were accidentally tripped. It was established that the trip had been caused by a battery locomotive working within a permanent-way possession entering a dead overhead electrical section with its pantographs raised.

292 Following the problems encountered by the Tyne & Wear Metro during its early years when it was discovered that earth leakage currents (stray currents) were giving rise to interference with sensitive instruments in Newcastle University, it has been the practice for HMRI to chair a working party which considers the effects of such stray currents for that system. This practice was then followed for Manchester Metrolink but not for Sheffield Supertram. However in the light of what has since occurred this may have been the wrong decision. For street running systems the statutory undertakers are concerned about the corrosive effects of such currents on their apparatus and the design of the traction power supply system has had, as one of its objectives, the minimisation of stray currents.

293 A second problem arose in Manchester, that of the effect such a current would have on the signalling track-circuits on British Railways. It was considered that the attenuation of a spurious 50 Hz signal being generated by the propulsion circuits in the LRV was such that maloperation of the adjacent ac track circuits on BR on the approach to Manchester Victoria was so remote that it could be neglected. However, remedial measures were taken for the low-voltage track-circuits in Manchester Piccadilly Station because measurements of possible earth-leakage current proved to be unreliable in the limited time available for testing.

294 This is not the case however with Sheffield Supertram where the LRT system track runs parallel to, but at varying distances from, non-electrified tracks of British Railways. On the line to Meadowhall the two railways run very close together and full immunisation of the BR track circuits was necessary. However the case for providing full immunisation of the tracks in Sheffield Midland Station where Supertram will run on an embankment or viaduct some 5 m or more above BR is less clear-cut. Modelling techniques were used to try to assess the driving voltage needed to cause maloperation of the low voltage dc track circuits. This demonstrated that fairly high voltages were necessary and that it ought to be possible to eliminate these by careful design of the track formation and of the traction power supply system, in particular, the arrangements for the return current. Nevertheless it is possible for a series of faults to exist which would give rise to an unacceptable risk. Clearly more study of this problem is needed so that unwarranted costs in immunising signalling equipment on adjacent railways are not incurred.

The management of safety

295 Although there had been some advance phases, the internal restructuring of BR's operations under the banner 'Organisation for Quality' was effectively complete at the beginning of April 1992, but note paragraph 13 of the Introduction regarding description of locations in this report. The practical effect of this change was to divide BR into individual businesses with profit centres within those businesses to be managed as independently as possible within the overall policies of BRB.

296 This report last year mentioned some concerns for the future management of safety but reported some of the steps which were being taken to ensure that standards were not eroded by the change. In fact the outcome has been mixed and probably has depended more on the attitude and culture of individual managers and their supporting teams than on the central culture expressed in the Board's Safety Plan.

297 Inspectors in the field have, often by invitation, made more advisory visits than ever before to address groups of managers, supervisors and staff to advise and guide them about their duties under health and safety legislation. The desire for guidance is to be welcomed but the fact that the capacity to satisfy it was lacking internally is not. Other branches of HMRI also noted a drop in the quality of submissions from some parts of the re-organised railway and a greater need for advice to be given by HMRI because new job-holders had not been fully and adequately trained.

298 Despite these criticisms it must be stated that the accident record improved in some respects through this difficult period, but much remains to be done to drive personnel accidents down to an acceptable level; some of the efforts are described as follows.

BR track safety initiative

299 A most important project started by BR in this year was an in-depth study of the safety of workers on the line who, historically, have suffered a fatal accident rate as great as some of the most dangerous industries. A senior manager, Mr G Eccles, re-analysed in-depth all such fatal accidents over 10 years, and studied practice elsewhere in the world. He made a series of recommendations for the future, some of which are quite radical and require significant changes in methods of work and railway operations. As a result, not all of these can easily be implemented and some need to be set alongside other track safety initiatives to compare their individual and cumulative values, but the debate generated is itself useful in focussing attention on this most important issue and HMRI is strongly encouraging and supporting this work.

Activities of RIAC

300 The Railways Industry Advisory Committee (RIAC) is the industry advisory committee which provides HSC with advice on occupational health and safety in the railway industry. The Chief Inspecting Officer of Railways acts as Chairman of the Committee and an Assistant Chief Inspecting Officer chairs the RIAC Track Safety Working Group (TSWG). Following the transfer of the Railway Inspectorate to HSE the Secretary of State for Transport also looks to HSC and RIAC for guidance on issues of passenger safety.

301 Amongst the main issues dealt with by RIAC during this period was the Appleton Report into fire and bomb related stoppages on LUL and BR systems mentioned in last year's report. RIAC welcomed the report and endorsed both the general approach taken and the conclusions reached. The Committee particularly supported the recommendation that regulation of fire safety on the railways should be based on an all risks assessment approach.

302 In August and November 1992 RIAC provided a forum for discussion of the draft report *Ensuring safety on Britain's railways*. RIAC comments provided additional input into the HSE recommendations to HSC about the post-privatisation safety regime.

303 Although responsibility for managing safety rests with railway operators, RIAC undertook its annual review of progress on the development of safety management systems, and helped to identify essential characteristics for safety management practice.

Track Safety Working Group

304 The TSWG continued its work of sharing knowledge and opinion in the matter of personal safety on the line among the principal railway operators and trades union representatives. In particular it drafted industry-wide guidance on the subject for publication by HSC. Not surprisingly a number of the Group's recommendations, especially regarding the separation of staff at work from the danger of trains, parallel those being developed internally by BR as a result of the Eccles Report. The need to facilitate temporary blockage of a line to trains while staff are at risk on it is seen by all concerned as a paramount issue to be tackled.

Occupational Health Working Group

305 The Occupational Health Working Group continued work on the production of guidance for:

(a) manual handling in the railway industry;

(b) trauma counselling within the railway industry; and

(c) occupational health issues for small railway operators.

New health and safety legislation

306 In January 1993 a tranche of new regulations derived from EC directives, colloquially known as 'the six-pack', became law. Most importantly, and underpinning all others, is the Management of Health and Safety at Work Regulations 1992 which requires all significant risks to be identified, assessed and where necessary, preventive and control measures to be put in place. However this process needs to be guided. In addressing risks on a wide front, priorities should be identified. The greater effort needs to be directed towards the greatest risks. Also, in a large geographically spread industry like the railways, the same issues may be addressed over and over again in different places by different managers. The railway companies must seek to ensure that they achieve a proper result in an efficient manner without needless duplication of effort. If managed effectively the procedure should enable safety issues to be tackled with a vigour and effort proportionate to the risk, which has not always been the case hitherto. Specific issues which are now being more vigorously addressed in response to the new regulations include manual handling, which is a major source of injury in railway work, and falls from a height, especially from the roofs of railway rolling stock, which have a significant potential for death or serious injury.

Table 13A Staff fatal and serious injury movement accidents 1992/93

Place	Date	Consequence	Possession	Environment	Agent of injury
Derby (RTC)	11.08.92	Fatal	No	Daylight	Propelled movement (during shunting)
Midcalder	31.08.92	Fatal	Yes - (one line only)	Darkness	Service train at speed
Mostyn	11.11.92	Serious injury	Yes - (one line only)	Darkness	Service train at speed
Cockburnspath	31.01.93	Serious injury	Yes - (on both lines)	Darkness	Propelled movement of engineer's train
Forth Bridge	07.03.93	Fatal	Yes - (one line only)	Daylight	Service train on 'wrong' line
Radlett	07.03.93	Fatal	Yes - (on both lines)	Darkness	Propelled movement of engineer's train
Pevensey	17.03.93	Fatal	Yes - (one line only)	Darkness	Service train at speed

Personnel accident record

General

307 This section deals solely with accidents to railway and contractors' employees. The relevant statistics are tabulated in Appendix 2 and included in more detail in Appendices 5, 6 and 7 for train accidents, movement and non-movement accidents respectively.

308 The total of 11 fatalities for the 12-month period April 1992 to March 1993 is the lowest ever recorded. This is encouraging but it is accepted by all concerned that more can and should be done to reduce these numbers.

309 Excluding a single fatality caused by a train accident and another during shunting activities the remaining nine deaths occurred at sites of planned engineering work. Five persons were killed in circumstances connected with their particular engineering occupation and four killed in train movement accidents within or alongside possessions of the line. There were also several serious injury accidents with similar characteristics.

310 It is a poor reflection on safety management to have such a high proportion of fatal accidents at sites where the work has been planned in advance. In some cases the plan of work was an unsafe one, in some it was not executed in accordance with the current rules, in others alterations to the plan in the course of its execution led to danger, but unsafe actions by individuals also played a part in a number of them.

311 All these shortcomings point to a need for more vigorous and active safety management leading to safe plans executed by well-trained and competent supervisors backed by systematic monitoring. A higher level of risk-awareness is also needed throughout the organisation. Lack of awareness or disregard of the risks from unsafe actions is still too common in the 'macho' world of railway maintenance, especially, as is often the case, when work is carried out within specific time constraints.

312 The total of notifiable staff accidents remained almost static during the year at 3643. Non-movement accidents formed the bulk at 3423 with the most common cause being slips, trip or falls followed closely by injuries suffered when handling, lifting or carrying, highlighting clearly the importance of attention to manual handling now required by statute.

Train accidents

313 The single fatality in a train accident was the driver of a loaded coal train which collided with the rear of a stationary empty freight train held at a signal. A proving circuit on level crossing barriers ahead of the stationary train had failed. The accident occurred about two miles south of *Morpeth (ER)*, Northumberland, and is more fully described elsewhere in this report.

Movement accidents

314 Table 13A shows some of the characteristics of movement accidents to

Table 14   Fatalities to staff through being struck by trains while at work on or about the track

Cause	92/93	91/92	1990	1989	1988	1987
(a) protection inadequate	2	3	2	2	1	1
(b) lookoutman at fault	-	-	-	-	1	-
(c) acted incorrectly after seeing or being warned of train	1	1	6	1	1	-
(d) unaware of train owing to lack of vigilance	1	1	2	1	2	3
(e) remaining	-	1	1	0	1	4
Total	4	6	11	4	6	8

Note: The fatal accident to a shunter at Derby is not included in this table.

employees which resulted in death or serious injury during the year. Some features recur, and these are amplified in the remarks that follow.

315 The accident at the *Railway Technical Centre* at *Derby* involved a man controlling a propelled shunting movement from the ground. There were no witnesses but it is surmised that he must have lost his footing and fallen under the wheels of the train. The driver had lost sight of the shunter before the accident; in accordance with the rules he should have stopped but did not do so.

316 The accidents at *Midcalder (ScR)*, Lothian, and *Mostyn (LMR),* near Flint, Clwyd, both involved men struck when working beside on-track machines at night while the adjacent line was open to traffic. In neither case was adequate protection in place and in the case of the Midcalder accident an intended safety measure, that trains would only pass at 20 mile/h, was not effectively put in place either. HMRI has expressed its grave concern to the railway about these and prosecuted BRB after the Midcalder accident. This whole issue is being addressed with the major track safety initiative described earlier; meanwhile HMRI is seeking to ensure at local level that possessions of the line are managed with proper regard for safety.

317 As is so often the case there were several other factors in each accident, adding cumulatively to the obvious risk described in paragraph 316. The accidents at *Cockburnspath (ScR)*, Border Region, and *Radlett (LMR)*, Hertfordshire, also both in darkness, were in double-line possessions and the agent of death or injury was in each case an engineer's train being propelled by its locomotive without the driver, or anyone else, having an adequate view ahead. After an improvement notice was served relating to the management of propelling in possessions, BR has been purposefully analysing this matter, with a view to minimising propelling movements and, where they are necessary, providing suitable equipment and systems of work to ensure safety in such operations.

318 The fatal accident on the *Forth Bridge (ScR)*, Firth of Forth, was perplexing and distressing since, like another such accident in 1991, it involved a man walking on the unsafe side, adjacent to the line remaining open to trains, and then being struck by a train from behind him running in the 'wrong' direction.

The difference between the previous accident and this one is that steps had been put in place, and were applied in this case, to ensure that no one went onto the bridge without a safety briefing including, where relevant, details of which line was blocked and which was open to traffic. Further control measures were put in place following this accident and an alternative means of access is being developed which should significantly reduce the need to walk beside the line on the bridge.

319 At *Pevensey and Westham (SR)*, East Sussex, a leading trackman assisting with track welding duties stepped from a position of safety into the path of a Down passenger train and was killed. The Up line of the double line section had been blocked for the engineering possession.

320 Table 14 is updated for this report but probably is shown for the last time as its value is now limited. The causes of accidents are often more complex, and other factors may have greater significance than this table suggests.

Non-movement accidents

321 The four non-movement accidents in which there were five fatalities also amply confirm that safe plans of work and competent supervision are necessary to maintain safe methods of working and avoid risk.

322 In June, during the demolition of a three-span brick arch bridge at *St John's Station (SR)*, Greater London, two members of the demolition contractor's staff working under the bridge were killed when the bridge collapsed in an uncontrolled manner. An inspecting officer, who is a chartered civil engineer, investigated the accident and provided technical advice to the British Transport Police (BTP) who subsequently passed a file to the CPS. It was decided that no manslaughter charges would be brought but parties are still liable to be charged under the Health and Safety at Work etc Act 1974.

323 At *Christchurch (SR)*, Dorset, during an afternoon in *July,* three members of a permanent way gang decided to move a 60-foot flat bottomed rail to a more convenient position for cutting. One member of the gang while attempting to turn the rail upright with a crowbar in a fishbolt hole was struck in the neck by the bar and suffered a fatal injury. The potential for serious injury had already

been recognised by British Railways and turning rails with a bar in this way was prohibited. A rail turning bar is provided to track staff which will release a rail safely in the event of any sudden forward movement.

324 In December, one member of a gang of overhead line maintenance staff working at *Barking (AR)*, Greater London, came into contact with a live section of 25 kV overhead line and died from injuries received. The work undertaken, removal of redundant switchgear on a portal type structure was not scheduled for that engineering possession and consequently the planned electrical isolation did not afford a safe system of work for the unscheduled task. In this instance there was a failure to recognise the limits of protection provided by the permit-to-work.

325 Also in *December*, during the course of demolishing the roof of a single-storey shunters' cabin at *Kings Lynn (AR)*, Norfolk, a contractor was killed when the roof unexpectedly collapsed. The contractors had failed to appreciate that their actions had weakened the structure of the ends of the supporting beams. A method statement was not produced because of the small-scale nature of the work involved.

Table 15 Prosecutions brought by HM Railway Inspectorate heard during 1992/93

Defendant	Date of offence and location	Legislation breached	Penalty imposed	Nature of incident leading to offence
British Railways Board and Survey & Construction (Roofing) Ltd	12.2.92 Ramsgate Traction and Rolling Stock Depot	HSW Act S4(2) Construction (working places) Reg 35(4)	£750 £1000	Member of contractor's staff fell from unprotected edge of roof sustaining serious injuries.
British Railways Board	20.12.91 Thornaby Traction Maintenance Depot	HSW Act S2(1) Factories Act S27(5)	£1750 on each of 2 charges	Electric chain hoist fell from its runway when misused and overloaded.
British Railways Board	10.4.91 Craigendoran	HSW Act S2(1) S3(1)	£25 000 on each of 2 charges	Passenger and goods trains collided, several passengers and employees injured, due to faulty wiring of points.
British Railways Board	14.6.91 Brickyard foot crossing	HSW Act S3(1) S33(1)	£1000 on each of 2 charges	Breach of improvement notice. Failure to maintain foot crossing.
British Railways Board	12.3.92 Derby Station	HSW Act S2	£5000	Tow tractor driven off platform edge by unauthorised operator.
British Railways Board	8.4.92 Primrose Hill	HSW Act S2(1)	£16 000*	BR employee struck a buried 25 000V cable.
Shank & McEwan Contractors Ltd	26.4.92 Cockburnspath	HSW Act S2(1) S33(1)(a)	Admonished	Beam fell from bridge abutment during construction.

* The maximum penalty for most HSW Act offences tried in a magistrates court increased from £2000 to £20 000 on 1.4.92

Capstan-powered rope haulage is used to move coaches onto this traverser. The Inspectorte is discussing with BR safer methods of stopping than that employing 'scotchers', as shown in the second photograph.

326 Of the 3423 non-movement accidents, 245 of which resulted in major injuries, the main causes were 20% attributed to slipping, tripping and falling, 17% to manual handling and lifting and 9% were assaults while on duty.

327 Especially on or near the line, the same underfoot conditions which give rise to risk of falling over can also contribute to manual handling accidents as workers stumble while carrying heavy weights. While many new access points have been created, with steps where necessary on bank sides, cesses at the lineside have tended to deteriorate and not be maintained. Their restoration and maintenance in future would enhance safety at several levels, from avoidance of risks of falling over through to avoidance of being struck by trains. The Inspectorate is not satisfied with the present position and is seeking greater commitment from the railways in this area.

The work of field inspectors

Staffing

328 The field force at April 1992 comprised four Principal Inspecting Officers (PIOs) and 13 Inspecting Officers (IOs) under the general direction of the Assistant Chief Inspecting Officer (ACIO) responsible for health and safety enforcement. To assist the ACIO with the development of HSW policy and liaison within HSE a Principal Inspector of Factories has been seconded from another branch of HSE.

329 During the year a further seven new IOs were appointed and another vacancy filled temporarily by a Factory Inspector on secondment. One IO promoted to the grade of PIO has temporarily been given responsibility for HSW Act enforcement at the site of the Channel Tunnel works.

Accident prevention work

330 The four teams of field inspectors continued to carry out preventive inspections of workplaces and work practices, especially transient work, as its highest priority. In 1992/93 the number of planned inspections was 1452, a decrease from the previous year, but the method of recording was changed in respect of transient work sites which account for about 25% of the inspections. Visits to area supervisors rather than to individual mobile gangs were recorded. The field inspectors continued with many other activities, such as advisory work, accident investigation and investigating public and railway staff complaints. They also played an increasing role in new works inspections and inspecting minor railways following the retirement of the inspector who formerly dealt exclusively with them.

Formal HSW Act enforcement actions

General policy

331 Most managers are anxious to comply with the law and a growing number realise the benefits of good heath and safety management. In such cases an inspecting officer will usually be pleased to offer guidance and encouragement. If evidence is found that the law is being broken the inspector can respond in various ways. He may instruct or warn by letter, issue a prohibition or improvement notice requiring immediate compliance or compliance within a certain specified time, or prosecute.

332 An improvement notice is usually only used where there is doubt about the necessary improvements being made to comply with the law or when improvements previously agreed to are not made. A notice is unlikely if compliance is achieved voluntarily in a reasonable time. A prohibition notice is only served where there is a risk of serious personal injury and no effective action is being taken voluntarily by the person in charge.

333 A prosecution is pursued only where there have been grave inadequacies in the application of appropriate safety measures. It may be sought if a breach has significant potential for harm, regardless of whether it caused an injury. A guilty verdict highlights a failure of systems to manage safety adequately and is a public condemnation of such deficiencies.

Prosecutions

334 Table 15 shows the prosecutions brought by the Inspectorate with a court hearing between April 1992 and March 1993.

Failed road crane which had been assisting another, immobilised in muddy ground.

Other actions

Safety from trains

335 Measures in hand to enhance the safety of staff on the line are largely identified in earlier paragraphs. It is sufficient to reiterate here that this remains a high priority issue in the work of field inspectors and, while a good momentum of thinking and talking about safety at working level has been built up, the Inspectorate is concerned to ensure that this is sustained. BRB shares this concern and dialogue on this most important subject continues at all levels. Major changes on an individual level to attitudes and understanding are sought, and at an organisational level changes to systems of work for greater segregation of workers from moving trains are being planned. Neither of these can be achieved quickly but the Inspectorate tries to maintain the pace of change.

Conductor rail safety

336 Particularly since the Electricity at Work Regulations 1989 came into force the Inspectorate has focussed increasing attention on employee safety in relation to conductor rails where they exist, mainly on London Underground and the former Southern Region of BR.

337 The Inspectorate has been concerned about both the frequency of accidents involving conductor rails and the indifferent attitude of some railway staff to the dangers of the live rail. There is an ever present risk of a fatal accident unless appropriate precautions are taken; fortunately there were no such fatalities to staff in the year but there were 19 notifiable injury accidents and the Inspectorate is aware of a number of other incidents of significant potential hazard.

338 The Inspectorate has given senior managers advice, comments, and where necessary applied pressure to develop a complete revision of BRB dc electrified lines' working instructions. The instructions deal mainly with isolation procedures and permits to work. Also being revised, in parallel, are the safe systems of work necessary to work alongside a live conductor rail. Previously such work had not been subject to assessment and staff did not have the benefit of written systems of work, describing the measures necessary to avoid danger.

339 Similarly, London Underground Limited has produced a series of electrified-track data sheets with the objective of making permanent way staff aware of the hazards that traction current presents, what work is permissible with the conductor rails live, how to avoid danger during such work and what action to take if someone is electrocuted or receives an electric shock.

340 Both on BR and LUL, considerable efforts by managers and supervisors are needed to ensure that the safe systems now specified are actually adopted and used routinely, in contrast to the habitual disregard of risk which inspectors formerly observed.

Work on overhead electrified lines

341 A robust permit-to-work system has always been used to ensure the electrical safety of work on BR's 25 kV overhead traction system. The only notifiable staff accident involving contact with live equipment was the one at Barking, where a man died when work outside the isolation was attempted.

342 The safety of working at heights on the overhead equipment has been of more concern to the Inspectorate, the most dangerous practice being working off loose ladders, with the attendant risks of falling, and doing so on an operational line under look-out protection, with a risk of failing to clear persons and the ladder from the path of a train. Under pressure from the Inspectorate considerable steps have been taken to minimise these risks. First, the use of ladders has been significantly reduced and rail-mounted elevating work platforms substituted to a large degree, secondly, where ladders are used, safety harnesses which can be clipped to parts of the OLE have been introduced, and thirdly, the use of ladders on lines open to trains has virtually been eliminated.

343 A remaining hazardous practice, of working from the flat roofs of overhead line trains without protection against falls, is being addressed during the year 1993/94. Apart from potentially being in breach of the HSW Act, unsafe practices giving rise to risk of falling are also addressed in The Workplace (Health, Safety and Welfare) Regulations 1992.

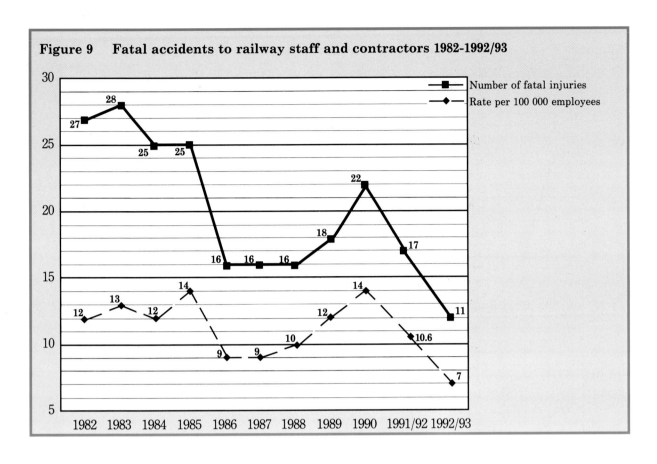

Figure 9   Fatal accidents to railway staff and contractors 1982-1992/93

- Number of fatal injuries
- Rate per 100 000 employees

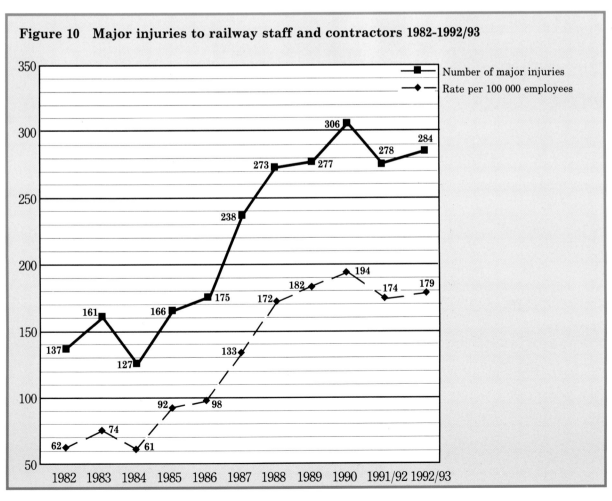

Figure 10   Major injuries to railway staff and contractors 1982-1992/93

- Number of major injuries
- Rate per 100 000 employees

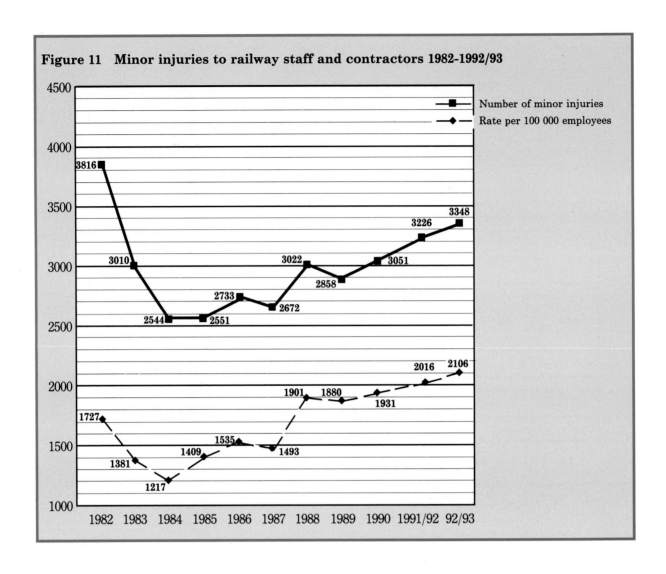

Figure 11   Minor injuries to railway staff and contractors 1982-1992/93

Legend:
- Number of minor injuries
- Rate per 100 000 employees

Number of minor injuries data points: 3816, 3010, 2544, 2551, 2733, 2672, 3022, 2858, 3051, 3226, 3348

Rate per 100 000 employees data points: 1727, 1381, 1217, 1409, 1535, 1493, 1901, 1880, 1931, 2016, 2106

Years: 1982, 1983, 1984, 1985, 1986, 1987, 1988, 1989, 1990, 1991/92, 92/93

Accidents and failures, numbers of staff and operating statistics

	Train accidents	Failures of rolling stock and permanent way	Railway staff	Train miles operated				Passenger journeys (including season tickets)		Passenger miles (estimate)	
				Total	British Railways		Metropolitan Railways*	British Railways	Metropolitan Railways*	British Railways	Metropolitan Railways*
					Passenger	Freight					
	Number		Thousands	Million train miles				Millions		Millions	
1988	1330	1324	159	313	209	66†	38	753	874	21 115	4391
1989	1434	1499	152	303	224	47†	32	743	856	20 735	3934
1990	1283	1776	158	302	231	37†	34	762	783	20 624	3882
1991/92	960	1609	160	313	219	54†	40	762	825	19 920	4140
1992/93	1152	1862	159	311	228	37†	46	769	787	19 709	3893

* Metropolitan Railways include Tyne & Wear Metro, London Underground Railways, Strathclyde Glasgow Underground Railway and Docklands Light Railway
† Includes empty coaching stock working

Casualties in all accidents

	Killed					Major injuries					Minor injuries				
	1992/93	1991/92	1990	1989	1988	1992/93	1991/92	1990	1989	1988	1992/93	1991/92	1990	1989	1988
Total all accidents	50	94	84	69	97	536	495	550	569	596	9699	9156	9998	10 232	10 270
Passenger	28	58	39	33	69	238	192	224	268	309	6125	5788	6238	7170	7062
Railway staff*	11	17	22	18	16	284	278	306	277	273	3348	3226	3051	2858	3022
Other persons†	11	19	23	18	12	14	25	20	24	14	226	142	209	204	186
Train accidents															
Total	5	11	4	18	40	13	30	22	58	84	140	361	221	346	621
Passengers	–	2	–	6	34	3	18	13	39	75	63	289	144	272	540
Railway staff*	1	2	1	6	2	5	6	6	18	6	69	59	67	53	62
Other persons†	4	7	3	6	4	5	6	3	1	3	8	13	10	21	19
Movement accidents															
Total	38	73	75	41	53	116	113	157	131	139	2442	2247	2620	2638	2671
Passengers	26	53	37	25	34	79	73	107	97	102	2335	2181	2551	2601	2619
Railway staff*	5	9	19	8	11	34	39	48	28	36	106	65	68	35	49
Other persons†	7	11	19	8	8	3	1	2	6	1	1	1	1	2	3
Non-movement accidents															
Total	7	10	5	10	4	407	352	371	380	373	7117	6548	6659	7248	6978
Passengers	2	3	2	2	1	156	101	104	132	132	3727	3318	3545	4297	3903
Railway staff*	5	6	2	4	3	245	233	252	231	231	3173	3102	2916	2770	2911
Other persons†	–	1	1	4	–	6	18	15	17	10	217	128	198	181	164

* Railway staff includes contractors' staff
† Excluding trespassers, suicides and attempted suicides

Train accidents and failures of rolling stock and permanent way

Index		All railways 1991/92	All railways 1992/93	1992/93 BR	1992/93 LUL & DLR	1992/93 Other railways
Index	**Train accidents total**	960	**1152**	1092	**22**	**38**
	Total collisions	187	**154**	151	1	2
	Collisions between:					
*1	Passenger trains or parts thereof	10	6	5	–	1
*2	Passenger trains and freight trains or light locomotives	3	1	1	–	–
*3	Freight trains, light locomotives or other moving vehicles**	14 (6)	11 (8)	11 (8)	– (–)	– (–)
4	Trains and vehicles standing foul of line**	– (–)	1 (–)	1 (–)	– (–)	– (–)
*5	Trains and buffer stops or vehicles standing at buffer stops**	31 (–)	25 (–)	23 (–)	1 (–)	1 (–)
6	Trains and projections from other trains or vehicles on parallel lines†	129 (112)	110 (95)	110 (95)	– (–)	– (–)
	Total derailments	144	**205**	175	2	28
	Derailments:					
*7	of passenger trains	23	30	11	2	17
*8	of freight trains**	121 (65)	175 (107)	164 (105)	– (–)	11 (2)
	Total running into obstructions	340	**532**	520	6	6
9	Trains running into:					
	(a) gates or vehicles or animals at level crossings	40	33	33	–	–
	(b) animals on the line	110	112	112	–	–
	(c) other obstacles	190	387	375	6	6
	Total fires in trains	225	**202**	187	13	2
10	Fires in trains:					
	(a) passenger trains	192	178	163	13	2
	(b) freight trains	33	24	24	–	–
	Total other accidents†	64 (42)	**59 (32)**	59 (32)	– (–)	– (–)
11	Other accidents†	64 (42)	59 (32)	59 (32)	– (–)	– (–)

Index		All railways 1991/92	All railways 1992/93	1992/93 BR	1992/93 LUL & DLR	1992/93 Other railways
	Failures of rolling stock and permanent way etc total	1609	**1862**	1713	127	22
	Total for rolling stock	351	**375**	340	26	9
12	Failure of locomotives and multiple unit trains:					
	(a) diesel††	89 (4)	90 (2)	90 (2)	– (–)	– (–)
	(b) electric††	142 (28)	114 (4)	86 (4)	25 (–)	3 (–)
	(c) steam	–	–	–	–	–
13	General failures of rolling stock (excluding indices 14, 15 and 16)	46	76	75	–	1
14	Failures of wheels or tyres	20	19	18	1	–
15	Failures of axles	5	17	16	–	1
16	Failure of coupling apparatus:					
	(a) passenger	42	53	49	–	4
	(b) freight	7	6	6	–	–
	Total for permanent way and structures	1258	**1487**	1373	101	13
17	Failure of structures					
	(a) tunnels, bridges, viaducts, culverts, etc	29	46	38	7	1
	(b) damage to bridges etc by motor vehicles & ships	31	45	41	3	1
18	Failure of track:					
	(a) broken rails	729	724	681	41	2
	(b) track buckles	13	33	33	–	–
19	Flooding of permanent way, slips in cuttings, etc	119	208	195	11	2
20	Fires at passenger stations, signal boxes etc	116	150	112	37	1
21	Failures of overhead line equipment	39	30	26	–	4
22	Miscellaneous failures	182	251	247	2	2

Note: The index numbers correlate with those at Appendix 5
* Accidents considered significant when occurring on or affecting passenger lines
† Figures marked in brackets denote the number of open door collisions included in each total
** Figures marked in brackets denote the number of accidents which occurred on freight only lines or lines in the possession of the engineer included in each total
†† Figures marked in brackets denote the number of powered door failures included in each total not attributed to operator error or malicious action

Train accidents in 1992/93 analysis is by primary causes

	Total	Collisions	Derailments	Running into obstructions	Fires in trains	Other accidents
						59
Total	**1152**	**154**	**205**	**532**	**202**	**59**
Staff error – total	**218**	**48**	**95**	**60**	**4**	**11**
Train crews (including guards):						
(a) passing signals at danger	11	2	7	1	–	1
(b) other irregularities or want of care:						
(i) drivers	43	30	7	3	1	2
(ii) guards	3	–	1	–	–	2
(iii) drivers and guards	5	2	3	–	–	–
Signalmen:						
(a) irregular block working	–	–	–	–	–	–
(b) other irregularities or want of care	5	–	4	1	–	–
Other staff:						
(a) in traffic departments	22	3	16	3	–	–
(b) in other departments	103	3	42	50	3	5
Train crews and signalmen	11	4	7	–	–	–
Train crews and other staff	8	4	3	1	–	–
Signalmen and other staff	3	–	3	–	–	–
Faulty loading	4	–	2	1	–	1
Technical defects – total	**283**	**1**	**104**	**51**	**118**	**9**
Locomotive and multiple units	116	1	5	9	96	5
Vehicles	33	–	6	4	19	4
Track	92	–	76	16	–	–
Signalling apparatus	4	–	2	2	–	–
Overhead line equipment	15	–	–	14	1	–
Other structures	3	–	–	3	–	–
Combined defects	8	–	5	3	–	–
Traction and braking shocks	12	–	10	–	2	–
Other causes – total	**651**	**105**	**6**	**421**	**80**	**39**
Snow, landslides, floods, etc	40	–	3	37	–	–
Animals on line	51	–	–	51	–	–
Irresponsibility of the public						
(a) irregular opening of doors	136	102	–	–	–	34
(b) at level crossings	35	–	–	34	–	1
(c) malicious	266	3	2	196	63	2
(d) other	43	–	–	36	6	1
Miscellaneous and cause not determined	80	–	1	67	11	1

APPENDIX 5

Casualties in train accidents in 1992/93
analysis by type of accident

		Killed				Major injuries				Minor injuries			
		Total	Passengers	Railway staff†	Other persons	Total	Passengers	Railway staff†	Other persons	Total	Passengers	Railway staff†	Other persons
	Total	**5**	**–**	**1**	**4**	**13**	**3**	**5**	**5**	**140**	**63**	**69**	**8**
Index	**Total from collisions**	**1**	**–**	**1**	**–**	**4**	**2**	**2**	**–**	**69**	**45**	**24**	**–**
*1	Collisions between: Passenger trains or parts thereof	–	–	–	–	2	2	–	–	29	24	5	–
*2	Passenger trains and freight trains or light locomotives	–	–	–	–	–	–	–	–	6	4	2	–
*3	Freight trains, light locomotives or other moving vehicles	1	–	1	–	2	–	2	–	11	–	11	–
4	Trains and vehicles standing foul of the line	–	–	–	–	–	–	–	–	7	6	1	–
*5	Trains and buffer stops or vehicles standing at buffer stops	–	–	–	–	–	–	–	–	9	4	5	–
6	Trains and projections from other trains or vehicles on parallel lines	–	–	–	–	–	–	–	–	7	7	–	–
	Total from derailments	**–**	**–**	**–**	**–**	**–**	**–**	**–**	**–**	**4**	**2**	**2**	**–**
*7	Derailments of passenger trains	–	–	–	–	–	–	–	–	2	2	–	–
*8	Derailments of freight trains	–	–	–	–	–	–	–	–	2	–	2	–
	Total from running into obstructions	**4**	**–**	**–**	**4**	**8**	**–**	**3**	**5**	**56**	**16**	**32**	**8**
9	Trains running into obstructions: (a) at level crossings	4	–	–	4	5	–	–	5	27	6	14	7
	(b) and (c) elsewhere**	–	–	–	–	3	–	3	–	29	10	18	1
	Total from fires in trains	**–**	**–**	**–**	**–**	**–**	**–**	**–**	**–**	**10**	**–**	**10**	**–**
10	Fires in trains: (a) passenger trains	–	–	–	–	–	–	–	–	8	–	8	–
	(b) freight trains	–	–	–	–	–	–	–	–	2	–	2	–
	Total from other accidents	**–**	**–**	**–**	**–**	**1**	**1**	**–**	**–**	**1**	**–**	**1**	**–**
11	Other accidents	–	–	–	–	1	1	–	–	1	–	1	–

* Accidents considered significant when occurring on or affecting passenger lines
† Railway staff includes contractors' staff
** See Appendix 3 for details

Casualties in movement accidents in 1992/93
analysis by type of accident

Index		Total	Killed	Major injuries	Minor injuries
	Passengers total	**2440**	**26**	**79**	**2335**
1	Entering or alighting from trains	702	3	34	665
2	Falling off platforms and being struck or run over by train	50	8	6	36
3	Crossing the lines at stations	94	6	9	79
4	Opening or closing of carriage doors	635	–	8	627
5	Falling out of carriages during the running of trains	43	9	6	28
6	Other accidents	916	–	16	900
	Railway staff* total	**145**	**5**	**34**	**106**
1	**Shunting accidents:** Getting on or off, or falling off, moving locomotives wagons	1	–	1	–
2	Coming into contact with vehicles or fixed lineside objects when riding on locomotives, etc	1	–	1	–
3	Staff on train involved in a collision in sidings	5	–	–	5
4	Being caught between vehicles while coupling or uncoupling	4	–	1	3
5	Struck or caught between vehicles when walking on the line	1	–	–	1
6	Miscellaneous	4	1	1	2
7	**Accidents during the running of trains:** Getting on or off, or falling from, locomotives, wagons, etc	16	–	10	6
8	Coming into contact with fixed lineside objects when riding on trains, etc	–	–	–	–
9	Train staff while on board train	71	–	15	56
10	Miscellaneous	3	–	–	3
11	**Accidents to staff working on or about the track:** Struck by train, etc, when acting as lookoutman or handsignalman	–	–	–	–
12	Struck by trains, etc, when working on or about the track	6	2	3	1
13	Struck by trains, etc, when authorised to walk on the track	–	–	–	–
14	Struck by flying objects or out-of-gauge parts of a train	3	–	–	3
15	Miscellaneous	14	2	–	12
16	**Other movement accidents:** Struck by trains, etc, when required to cross the line on duty	–	–	–	–
17	Struck by trains, etc, when not required to walk on the track (including failure to use an authorised route)	–	–	–	–
18	Through movement of vehicles at which men were engaged	5	–	–	5
19	Miscellaneous	11	–	2	9
	Other persons† total	**11**	**7**	**3**	**1**
1	At level crossings	8	6	2	–
2	On business at stations or sidings	2	–	1	1
3	Miscellaneous	1	1	–	–

* Railway staff include contractors' staff
† Excluding trespassers, suicides and attempted suicides

Casualties in non-movement accidents in 1992/93 – analysis by type of accident

Index		Total	Killed	Major injuries	Minor injuries
	Passengers total	**3855**	**2**	**156**	**3727**
1	Ascending or descending steps and escalators at stations	1683	–	42	1641
2	Being struck by barrows, falling over packages, etc	42	–	2	40
3	Falling from platform onto line	82	1	2	79
4	Electric shock on electrified railways	8	–	7	1
5	Slips, trips and falls	1270	–	94	1176
6	Other accidents	800	1	9	790
	Railway staff* total	**3423**	**5**	**245**	**3173**
1	Contact with or being trapped by moving machinery or material being machined	41	–	6	35
2	Struck by moving, including flying or falling object, other than rails	297	–	34	263
3	Struck by moving vehicle (other than rail vehicle)	32	–	4	28
4	Struck against something fixed or stationary	123	–	3	120
5	Injured while handling, lifting or carrying, other than rails	587	–	6	581
6	Fall through a height of more than 2 metres	24	–	13	11
7	Fall through a height of 2 metres or less	177	–	26	151
8	Fall from a stationary rail vehicle	77	–	7	70
9	Slip, trip or fall on the same level	678	–	54	624
10	Trapped by something collapsing or overturning	23	3	1	19
11	Burnt or scalded, other than by chemical or electrical agents	26	–	2	24
12	Using power-driven hand tools	40	–	4	36
13	Using unpowered hand tools	147	1	11	135
14	Handling rails by manual or mechanical means	97	–	8	89
15	Electric shock or burns from plant or equipment	16	–	5	11
16	Electric shock or burns from live rail or electrified lines	19	–	7	12
17	Electric shock or burns from overhead electrification equipment	1	1	–	–
18	Harmed by lack of oxygen (eg drowning/asphyxiation)	3	–	1	2
19	Injured by explosion	3	–	1	2
20	Contact with or exposure to harmful substance	52	–	17	35
21	Assaulted while on duty	320	–	14	306
22	Miscellaneous	640	–	21	619
	Other persons† total	**223**	**–**	**6**	**217**
1	On business	141	–	6	135
2	Miscellaneous	82	–	–	82

* Railway staff include contractors and post office staff handling mail
† Excluding trespassers, suicides and attempted suicides

Casualties to trespassers, suicides and attempted suicides in 1992/93

	Total	Killed	Major injuries	Minor injuries
Movement accidents total	**267** **(4)**	**224** **(3)**	**36** **(1)**	**7 (–)**
Trespassers	153 (4)	122 (3)	26 (1)	5 (–)
Suicides and attempted suicides	114 (–)	102 (–)	10 (–)	2 (–)
Non-movement accidents total	**66 (16)**	**20** **(2)**	**36 (11)**	**10 (3)**

Trespassers
    (a) electric shock on electrified railways
        (i)   conductor rail system
        (ii) OLE system
    (b) other causes
	
	6 (4)
	9 (5)
	41 (7)
		
		2 (1)
		2 (1)
		10 (–)
			
			2 (2)
			6 (4)
			24 (5)
				
				2 (1)
				1 (–)
				7 (2)

Suicides and attempted suicides	10 (–)	6 (–)	4 (–)	– (–)
Totals in all accidents	**333 (20)**	**244** **(5)**	**72 (12)**	**17 (3)**

Note: Figures in brackets denote the number of children under the age of 16 years included in each total

APPENDIX 9

ABBREVIATIONS

The following abbreviations have been used:

ABCL	automatic barrier crossing, locally monitored
ac	alternating current
ACIO	Assistant Chief Inspecting Officer (of Railways)
AHB	automatic half-barrier
ALC	accommodation level crossing (private)
AOCL	automatic open crossing, locally monitored
AOCR	automatic open crossing, remotely monitored
AR	Anglia Region (of British Railways)
ARPS	Association of Railway Preservation Societies
ATC	automatic train control
ATO	automatic train operation
ATP	automatic train protection
AWS	automatic warning system
BR	British Rail
BRB	British Railways Board
BREL	British Rail Engineering Limited
BRUTE	British Rail Universal Trolley Equipment
BTP	British Transport Police
CCTV	closed circuit television
COSHH	Control of Substances Hazardous to Health Regulations 1988
CWR	continuous welded rail
dc	direct current
DCIO	Deputy Chief Inspecting Officer (of Railways)
DEMU	diesel-electric multiple-unit (passenger train unless otherwise described)
DIAS	Directorate of Information and Advisory Services (of HSE)
DLR	Docklands Light Railway
DMU	diesel multiple-unit (passenger train unless otherwise described)
DO	Dangerous Occurences
DOT	Department of Transport
EC	European Community
ECML	East Coast Main Line
ECS	empty coaching stock (train)
EHO	Environmental Health Officer
EMU	electric multiple-unit (passenger train unless otherwise described)
ER	Eastern Region (of British Railways)
FOD	Field Operations Division (of HSE)
FP	footpath (level crossing)
GLW	gross laden weight
GMML	Greater Manchester Metro Limited
HMFI	Her Majesty's Factory Inspectorate
HMRI	Her Majesty's Railway Inspectorate
HSC	Health and Safety Commission
HSE	Health and Safety Executive
HST	high speed train
HSW Act	Health and Safety at Work etc Act 1974

IE	Iarnrod Eireann (Irish Rail)
IECC	Integrated Electronic Control Centre
ILWS	Inductive Loop Warning System
IN	Improvement notice
IO	Inspecting Officer (of Railways)
ISRS	International Safety Rating System
LFCDA	London Fire and Civil Defence Authority
LMR	London Midland Region (of British Railways)
LRT	light rapid transit
LRV	Light Rail Vehicle
LT&S	London, Tilbury and Southend
LUL	London Underground Limited
MCB	manually controlled barrier (operated by a railway employee)
MG	manual gate (operated by a railway employee including those operated by trainmen)
MU	Multiple unit (train)
MWL	miniature warning light
NIR	Northern Ireland Railways
NSE	Network South East
OC	open crossing
OLC	occupation level crossing (private)
OLE	overhead line equipment
ORV	occupant of road vehicle
PICOW	Person in Charge of Works
PIO	Principal Inspecting Officer (of Railways)
PLC	public level crossing
PN	Prohibition notice
RAP	Remedial Action Projects
RIAC	Railway Industry Advisory Committee
RIDDOR	Reporting of Injuries, Diseases and Dangerous Occurences Regulations
S&C	switches & crossings
S&T	Signal & Telecommunications
ScR	Scottish Region (of British Railways)
SMS	safety management system
SPAD	signal passed at danger
SR	Southern Region (of British Railways)
SSI	solid state interlocking
T&W	Tyne & Wear Metro
TC	Track circuit
TCAID	Track Circuit Actuator Interference Detector
TLF	Trainload Freight
TSWG	Track Safety Working Group
UWC	user worked crossing with either gates or lifting barriers not manned by a railway employee (T) denotes telephone provided.
WCML	West Coast Main Line
WR	Western Region (of British Railways)
WSF	wrong side failure

NEW DEVELOPMENTS 1992/93

The electrified route mileages as at April 1993 were:

	BR	Met Rlys	Total
Route mileage	10 775	297	11 072
Track mileage			
without sidings	20 040	614	20 654
ac overhead	1 773	-	1 773
dc overhead	-	38	38
dc conductor rail	1 209	258	1 467

REGULATORY PROCEDURES

1   The jurisdiction of the Secretary of State under the regulatory acts affecting safety remains unchanged. The various functions and the acts regulating the procedure are set out below under four main headings.

Inspection

2   Under the Road and Rail Traffic Act 1933, no railway, part of a railway, any fixed works, or electric traction may be brought into use for passenger traffic without the approval of the Secretary of State. Large installations as well as new methods of signalling are also subject to the Secretary of State's approval. Before this is given, or as a condition, the works are inspected, and the inspecting officer may require any additions or alterations which he may consider necessary for the safety of the public and railway staff. New level crossings as well as alterations in the methods of protection at existing level crossings by orders made under the British Transport Commission Act 1957, the Transport Act 1968, or the Level Crossings Act 1983, are also subject to the Secretary of State's approval and are inspected prior to approval being given.

Safety rules and regulations

3   In accordance with the Regulation of Railways Act 1889, orders were made requiring the railways to adopt the block system on passenger lines, to provide interlocking between points and signals on such lines, and to equip all passenger trains with a continuous brake. Also, under the Regulation of Railways Act 1868, means of passenger communication must be provided on all trains running over 20 miles without a stop. These obligations are still in force. As part of the supervision exercised under inspection procedure, the Secretary of State's present functions under the 1889 Act are confined to granting exemptions from the orders in respect of block working where special conditions prevail.

4   The Railway Employment (Prevention of Accidents) Act 1900, empowers the Secretary of State to make rules with the object of reducing or removing the dangers and risks incidental to railway service. Certain rules on matters specified in the Act were made in 1902 and 1911.

5   The Secretary of State has no jurisdiction over the construction of rolling stock (except where specifically provided in the enabling legislation), the maintenance of permanent way or signalling equipment, or the qualifications of operating staff.

Accidents

6   Under the Regulation of Railways Act 1871, and the Railway Employment (Prevention of Accidents) Act 1900, all accidents to trains on statutory railways and all those involving death or injury on railway premises are reported to the Secretary of State under the Railways (Notice of Accidents) Order 1986 (SI No 2187), which came into force on 1 January 1987. The Secretary of State is empowered by these Acts to order an inquiry into any of the accidents so reported, and this is done when circumstances warrant it. Reports of all accident inquiries conducted under the 1871 Act are made public under the terms of the Act.

7   The Notice of Accidents Order requires all accidents to passengers or other persons to be reported, however slight their injuries may be, but accidents to railway staff or contractors' employees need only be reported when the injuries are such as to cause absence from ordinary work for more than three days. Personal injuries are classed as 'major' or 'minor'. The former is defined as: 'fractures other than a bone in the hand or foot; amputation of a hand or foot; amputation of a finger, thumb or toe; burns or electric shock requiring hospital treatment; loss of sight of an eye; loss of consciousness from lack of oxygen; decompression sickness; acute illness from exposure to a pathogen; admission into a hospital for treatment for more than 24 hours. Any person who is known to have died from injuries before the date of this report is included as a fatality.

8   Under Section 8 of the Act of 1871 the Secretary of State, if requested to do so by a coroner in England or Wales, appoints an assessor to assist at any inquest which may be held on a person killed in a railway accident. Assistance would similarly be afforded to a sheriff in Scotland if required under Section 4 of the Fatal Accidents and Sudden Deaths Inquiry (Scotland) Act 1976. A report is required to be made public by the assessor so appointed.

9   The Reporting of Injuries, Diseases and Dangerous Occurrences Regulations 1985 (SI No 2023) came into effect from 1 April 1986.

The latter Regulations redefined the term 'major injury'; the Railways (Notice of Accidents) Order 1986 incorporates the same definition so that statistics may be comparable between the railway and other industries. The Regulations made under the Health and Safety at Work etc Act 1974 apply to all work activities, not merely those in premises registered as factory premises or office, shop or railway premises, but accidents reportable under the railway legislation are not required to be reported separately. All railways are required to report dangerous occurrences as defined in the Regulations.

Agency agreements

10   Under the Health and Safety at Work etc Act 1974, the Department of Transport concluded an agreement with the Health and Safety Commission in respect of the application of the Act to railway workers. The agreement was effective from 1 April 1975 until 30 November 1990. The circumstances of the Railway Inspectorate's transfer to the Health and Safety Executive on 1 December 1990 were described in Chapter 1 of the 1990 report. From that date, a subsequent agreement came into effect between the Department and the Commission by means of which the Inspectorate performs several statutory functions on behalf of the Secretary of State for Transport. These include various duties under the railway regulatory acts, other railway and tramway legislation and the Channel Tunnel Act 1987.

Transport and Works Act 1992

11   The new order-making procedure established by this Act to replace private Bill procedure for authorising guided transport systems, inland waterways and works in the sea came into force on 1 January 1993. Other parts of the Act now in force include the new criminal offence of working on a railway or tramway while unfit through drink or drugs, provisions enabling the Secretary of State to sanction the stopping up or diversion of footpath or bridleway level crossings in the interests of public safety and powers to require the provision of bridges or tunnels to replace non-vehicular level crossings.

12   Regulations under the Act about the approval of new or altered works and rolling stock on railways and other guided transport systems are likely to be made by the end of 1993. Other parts of the Act still to be implemented include new provisions for the placing of signs and barriers at private level crossings. Regulations about this will be the subject of a consultation exercise in the autumn of 1993.

Printed and published in the UK by the Health and Safety Executive   12/93 C25